'It's lovely!'

As she stepped  glanced around  marring her expression. 'Is it a strain keeping up with the running costs of this place?'

'A strain?' Daniel made an effort to gather his thoughts. 'No...no, I live pretty frugally...'

He should just tell her now and get it over and done with. Why was he finding it so difficult?

Daniel looked into Cathy's sweet face. Fear, that was what it all boiled down to. Fear of losing her. He knew that as soon as he revealed the extent of his wealth things would change. Cathy was fragile, proud, defensive about her lack of money. She would look at the differences between them and think they were too wide, too vast. He didn't want that. He didn't want anything to spoil this wonderful beginning.

Laura Martin lives in a small Gloucestershire village with her husband, two young children and a lively sheepdog! Laura has a great love of interior design and, together with her husband, has recently completed the renovation of their Victorian cottage. Her hobbies include gardening, the theatre, music and reading, and she finds great pleasure and inspiration from walking daily in the beautiful countryside around her home.

Recent titles by the same author:

COMING HOME FOR CHRISTMAS
HIS PERFECT PARTNER

MARRYING A MILLIONAIRE

BY
LAURA MARTIN

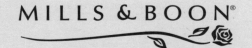

MILLS & BOON®

*First published in Great Britain 1999
Harlequin Mills & Boon Limited,
Eton House, 18-24 Paradise Road, Richmond, Surrey TW9 1SR*

© Laura Martin 1999

ISBN 0 263 81832 2

*Set in Times Roman 10½ on 11 pt.
02-9910-56367 C1*

*Printed and bound in Spain
by Litografia Rosés, S.A., Barcelona*

CHAPTER ONE

'MUMMY, tell me about our new house again!'

Cathy placed the last of her cooking utensils into the large cardboard box and sat back on her heels, glad of the diversion. She had been up since first light, making sure everything was organised for the move, and felt absolutely exhausted, even though it was barely three in the afternoon.

'Well, it's old, and it has four little windows at the front which look out onto a narrow lane, and there's a square of grass at the front and a much larger piece at the back...'

Robbie slid onto her lap and linked his arms around her neck. 'Tell me about the tree!'

Cathy smiled, cuddling him close. 'There's an apple tree in the front garden, just below your bedroom window, and soon it will have fluffy white blossom on it and later on there will be apples which we'll be able to pick any time we like.'

'And no one will tell us off?'

'No one will tell us off,' Cathy agreed.

'And we can pick the apples even if it's dark?'

Cathy laughed and kissed her son's cheek. 'Yes, even then.'

'I'm going to climb that tree, right to the top!'

'We'll see.'

A worried look flickered across Robbie's young face. 'And will there be friends for me to play with?'

'Oh, yes!' Cathy's expression was deliberately reassuring, for she knew this was an aspect of the move which was worrying Robbie greatly. 'There must be quite a lot of children in the village because they've got a lovely little school with a brand-new play area and a pond—'

'And if I don't like it we can come back here?'

Cathy pushed the curtain of fiery red hair back from her face and looked around the dismal kitchen, with its damp walls and cheap melamine units. If she had to endure even so much as another day in this box in the sky, then she felt she'd go stark raving mad.

She looked out of the window. From this position on the kitchen floor all she could see were grey lumpy clouds; there wasn't a tree in sight—no buildings either, come to that. Cathy heaved a sigh. Presumably somebody somewhere had thought it clever to put people in boxes instead of houses, and stack them so high that the tenants could actually feel the building swaying in the wind, but she couldn't for the life of her imagine why. A handy way of solving the housing problem, she supposed—except of course that living like this created more problems than it solved—far more.

Cathy thought of the graffiti and the litter and the smell which accompanied every journey to this, the twelfth floor; then she looked down at her son, snuggled on her lap. He would be able to read soon, and in no time the paint-sprayed words would begin to mean something and his sweet, mischievous innocence would be tainted before its time.

''Cos Dale says it's really boring in the countryside,' Robbie continued. 'He says there are no shops and if you want sweets then you have to walk *miles*! He says—'

'Well, when we're settled in you can invite Dale over and show him how good the countryside really is, can't you?' Cathy announced, before Robbie could repeat any more of his friend's little insights into country life. 'Don't worry, you're going to absolutely love it, sweetheart,' she told him with a cheerful smile. 'We both are.'

*   *   *

Daniel turned the collar up on his jacket. Hell! It was cold. He really needed to get the heating system mended on the Land Rover; three weeks of freezing March winds was as much as he could take. He drove past the garage which looked as if it had been caught in a time warp, with its singular petrol pump and its pre-war signs advertising anything from chocolate to washing powder, and mentally vowed to book it in first thing in the morning.

It was quiet in the village this evening; several lights were shining in the row of old cottages which lined the green, but few people were braving the rain on this cold, raw evening. Damn! Must get the brakes looked at too. He pressed his foot down hard on the pedal and the Land Rover came to a halt—eventually. Daniel regarded the van which blocked the lane for a moment—a rental vehicle, by the looks of things. The back was up and there was a small quantity of furniture inside which was getting wetter by the minute. Not exactly the best of times to move house.

He glanced towards the cottage. A single bulb dangled dismally from the ceiling in the front downstairs room. He knew the house—he knew all the properties in the village. It was rather run-down, in need of a total overhaul. The place had character—provided, that was, you could overlook the rotten windowpanes and moss-covered roof, and sundry other things that were doubtless in need of repair.

He exhaled a breath, regarding the vehicle with irritation. The lane was blocked and there was clearly still a fair amount of moving in to do. He'd have to turn around and take another route, which was annoying, considering he was less than half a mile from reaching his destination.

A man appeared at that moment, hurrying down the path from the house, wearing baseball cap and worn denims and a short leather jacket which did little to protect him from the torrential rain. The youth—for he was barely twenty, Daniel saw as he came nearer—glanced across at the Land Rover and hurried over. Daniel wound down his window.

'We're going to be a little while yet, mate. Not much

point in 'anging around.' A hard, assessing gaze. 'Not unless you fancy giving us an 'and, that is.' The young man
glanced back towards the house. 'Truth is, I'm a bit lumbered here.'

'Lumbered?' Daniel followed his gaze, watching as another figure, dressed more appropriately in a long yellow
mackintosh with hood pulled up, scurried down the path
towards the van.

'Yeah, I was let down by a mate.' The man wiped the
rain away from his eyes and turned his collar up, huddling
into the inadequate protection of his jacket. 'We've done
most of the small stuff, but now we've got a bed to shift,
and to be honest I don't see how we're going to do it.'

Daniel watched as the mackintosh-clad figure glanced
towards his vehicle, then clambered up into the van and
began to attempt to manoeuvre a bed towards the edge of
the van.

'Hey, don't be stupid! You'll do yourself an injury!' The
man's voice rang out sharply in the damp night air. He
glanced back at Daniel. 'See what I mean?' He swore
sharply as the bed teetered dangerously, then jogged over
to the van and hoisted himself up, issuing instructions in a
harsh, irritated voice.

Daniel exhaled a breath, glanced around the interior of
the Land Rover and retrieved a long, waxed raincoat, which
had definitely seen better days, from amongst the mess and
muddle in the back. It looked as if he was going to have
to help, or be witness to a rain-soaked disaster that wouldn't
be fit to sleep on tonight.

The bed wasn't particularly heavy, but it was awkward.
All the more so with the seemingly willing but rather in-
effectual helper in the yellow mackintosh getting in the
way. Daniel lifted the bed to the edge of the van, then
jumped down and helped the jacketed youth carry the item
down the garden path and into the house.

The interior was gloomy, and rather cold, but far better
than being out in the rain. Yellow Mackintosh led the way

like a beacon of light, and between them Daniel and the other man manoeuvred the bed through the narrow hallway and up a short flight of stairs to a large bedroom with faded pink rosebuds and several large damp stains on the walls.

'Thanks a lot. Just here will be fine.'

She sounded young and immensely grateful. Daniel wondered why the possibility of her being a woman hadn't occurred to him before. He gave the yellow mackintosh more than a cursory glance, watching with interest as the shrouded figure pulled down the hood to reveal a riot of crazy auburn curls which were a stark and colourful contrast against the shiny yellow material.

The girl was an amazing and vibrant apparition amongst the drabness of the house. Daniel found his gaze drawn to the delicate complexion, to the flash of emerald eyes. His mouth curved with surprise and the girl's mouth curved too, into a hesitant, shy smile. 'This is very good of you,' she murmured. 'I don't think we could have managed on our own, could we, Gary?'

'Nah. There's a couple more pieces.' 'Gary' raised questioning brows. 'Any chance of giving us a hand with those, mate? Then I can clear out of your way with the van.'

'Sure.' Daniel nodded. His gaze returned towards the girl. She looked exhausted. 'You might as well stay out of the rain,' he told her. 'No point in getting wet unneccesarily.'

'Thanks.' She managed another smile which, Daniel could see, involved some effort. 'I'd better go and check on Robbie. He'll be frightened if he wakes up and I'm not around.'

'Robbie?' The question was out before he realised.

'My son.' Steady green eyes met Daniel's enquiring gaze. 'He's asleep in a chair downstairs.' She glanced towards the youth. 'Gary, if you could get his bed next, that would be really helpful.'

'Yeah, OK, I'm doing my best.' He scowled. 'Can't promise anything.'

It took another thirty minutes before the last of the furniture was off-loaded from the van. It had been a rather scant haul: a few pieces of heavy, mismatched furniture and jumbled possessions.

'Thanks, mate. Couldn't have done it without you.' Gary let out a sigh of relief and proffered a somewhat grimy hand in thanks. 'If there was a pub around here, I'd buy you a pint.'

'There is, actually, but don't worry.' Daniel's mouth curved into a perfunctory smile. 'I'm on my way somewhere.'

'You're very wet. I'm so sorry we had to trouble you.'

He watched as she came into the front downstairs room. The mac had been removed to reveal ubiquitous, loose-fitting jeans and a baggy red jumper which clashed madly with her hair. In her arms was a child of about five or six, with silky brown hair and a cherub face. Daniel smiled. 'He's sleeping soundly.'

'Yes, thank goodness!' She glanced affectionately down at her son, then looked back at Daniel. 'I know it's not much, but would you like a cup of tea before you go? You've been so kind, helping us out like this. It's the least we can offer.'

Her voice was a great attraction: soft and soothing with a hint of huskiness. The sort of voice that stayed in your mind long after any words had been spoken. Daniel gazed for a few moments at mother and child, then, realising he was in danger of staring, made an effort and collected his thoughts. 'Thanks, but no, thanks. You've got your hands full enough as it is.' He smiled briefly. 'I'll leave you both to settle in.'

'And I'll shift the van.' Gary's voice was rough and harsh, over-loud in the echoey emptiness of the room. The child stirred in the young woman's arms.

'He's very tired. It's been a long day.' The girl inhaled

a steadying breath as she wrapped the blanket more tightly around her son, bending her head to kiss the silky brown hair. 'Goodbye, then.' Her eyelids were heavy with sleep. 'And thanks again.'

It was the strangest thing, Daniel mused as he hurried, head bent, through the still pouring rain to his Land Rover outside. Why on earth should he feel a compulsion to stay?

He opened the door and climbed in, waiting for Gary to move off in the van. He looked across at the uncurtained window. The house was dismal and cold. He thought of the girl and her son; presumably the two of them had some form of heating sorted out, but even so...

The van was moving. Daniel started his engine, allowed himself one last look across at the cottage, at the solitary light bulb swinging from the ceiling, realised suddenly that he didn't know her name, then thrust the battered vehicle into gear and pulled away.

All Cathy wanted to do was sleep—impossible, of course, with so much to do, but that was always the way of things. She'd had so many restless nights recently, worrying about the move, frightened to death that she wasn't doing the right thing, and now she felt dead on her feet.

She carried Robbie to the settee and settled him down beneath a pile of blankets; the mattress on his bed felt slightly damp, and she didn't want to risk giving Robbie a chill. She placed gentle fingers against his rosy cheek to check his temperature. He was as warm as toast, which was more than she could say for herself, she thought, as a shiver racked her body.

There was a cold draught of air coming from somewhere. She walked out into the narrow hall to investigate. Typical Gary; he hadn't shut the front door properly. She watched as he jogged back down the garden path. His trainers weren't as white as when he'd first started the move, she noticed; he wouldn't be pleased with that. 'I'll be getting back.' He huddled beneath the dilapidated porch, unsuccessfully trying to shelter from the driving rain.

'You don't want something to eat or drink before you go?' Cathy asked dutifully. She was relieved when he briefly shook his head. 'Nah, I need to get the van back.' He pulled back the cuff of his leather jacket and glanced down at his wristwatch. 'Marty wanted it back before nine, and it's gone that now.'

'OK.' Cathy leaned forward and kissed his cheek. 'You've been a great help. Come and see me, won't you, when I'm properly settled in?'

'Yeah, I might if I'm at a loose end.' He hesitated, glancing around into the gloom of the night. 'Although, why anyone would want to live out here in this Godforsaken wilderness I'll never know!'

'It's not a wilderness.' Cathy smiled. 'It's a beautiful village; there's a duck pond and a church, and a tiny shop which sells just about everything—'

'Yeah, well, it's your funeral...' Gary lifted his sloping shoulders in a shrug. 'Me—I'd go mad. And what about Robbie?'

'He's going to be fine about the move,' Cathy replied, with more conviction than she felt. 'Once he settles in, sees how much more enjoyable life can be in the country, he'll be fine.'

'Yeah! So you keep saying.' Gary turned away, clearly uninterested. 'Anyway, I'll see you.'

'Yes, bye!' Her voice, she thought, sounded forlorn in the dark night. Cathy waited until the van had pulled away, then closed the door on the dark, rainy night, conscious, as the silence engulfed her, that the moment she had been waiting for had finally arrived.

She wandered back into the front room, her gaze skimming over the faded wallpaper and dingy surfaces. Funny how much better things seemed when the sun was shining and the birds were singing, and you were caught in the grip of excitement about the new start in life you were going to make.

She stood in the middle of the room and listened. It was so quiet. Nothing. Not the distant hum of traffic or the banging of car doors, or people shouting. Silence. It was going to take a bit of getting used to after the continual noise of the estate. Cathy inhaled a deep breath. Gary was right; Robbie was going to miss his friends. He had just started school, got used to everything, and she had whisked him away from all that was familiar to try and fulfil some crazy, hare-brained dream of living in the country.

She thought about the impromptu farewell her friends and neighbours had given her just before she'd left. It had been such a nice surprise. Everyone had gone to so much trouble: baking a cake, wrapping up some simple house-warming presents, telling her how much they were going to miss her.

She turned towards the kitchen to search for a bucket and mop. There was a piece of wrapping paper still caught around the handle and she picked it off absent-mindedly.

He had been *so* handsome…tall and muscular in comparison to Gary's wiry frame…dark eyes, warm smile, large, capable hands…older than herself… Cathy reached into a box and pulled out a large bottle of cleaning fluid. Thirty, maybe… She turned on the hot tap and water splashed into the bucket; it was freezing cold. Such a relief when he had helped. She had been worrying about the move ever since Gary had turned up at the flat without his so-called mate. He had been on his way somewhere. A glimpse of a jacket beneath the old coat he'd worn, smart trousers, polished shoes. To visit a girlfriend, perhaps? Or just home from work, straight to a restaurant to meet his wife for dinner?

There was a restaurant on the green. Cathy had noticed it when she had first visited this place. It was very refined and expensive-looking, way out of her league—she could barely stretch to a bag of chips. Not that any of that mattered. She had moved here fully prepared for the struggle which lay ahead. Money was important, but only to the extent that she could pay her bills on time, earn enough so that Robbie was warm and clothed and well-fed. She knew she would have been better off staying in the flat in town— financially at least—but what about the quality of their lives? That mattered too, didn't it?

She glanced down at the picture on the bottle in her hand: a gleaming sink, sparkling taps. She gazed at the grimy work surfaces in front of her and jerked into action. She would need to boil lots of kettles for hot water, then she'd begin upstairs in Robbie's room. If she was lucky, by morning she might have the most important rooms cleaned and ready for habitation…

It was late. Daniel negotiated the narrow lanes with care, even though he felt like driving fast. That was what an evening spent with his parents did to him—or more particularly with his mother. He released an exasperated breath. When would she learn? More to the point, when would he? How many times had he fallen into the same trap? 'Just a few friends round for dinner, darling. Can you come? Nothing too grand. I need another man to make up numbers. And besides…'—and this was where guilt always made him fall for it—'…it's been so long since we last saw you…'

The rain was still heavy, lying on the road in places, splashing up against the sides of the battered Land Rover as he turned right into the village once again. It was a ghastly night—not made any better by having spent almost three hours having to endure his mother's unsubtle attempts at matchmaking.

Poor Lucy. Nice girl, as long as you were prepared to spend half the night talking about horses and the other half discussing the merits of various kinds of retail outlets— Harrods or Harvey Nichols? He replayed her voice in his head. Goodness, it really was *so* difficult to choose.

Daniel yawned, dragging a hand through his dark hair. Hell, he was tired. He glanced at the clock on his dashboard—almost eleven-thirty. He thought of his own place, situated in a quiet spot at the far end of the green. Nearly there. He hoped the fire would still be on—he'd banked it up well with wood before he'd left so it ought to be. A little relaxing music and a stiff drink before he hit the sack. Alone.

There was no doubt Lucy had been attractive. His mother, for some obscure reason, felt he had a penchant for long blonde hair and blue eyes. Daniel's mouth curved into a smile. Not a bad guess. Trouble was, long blonde hair and blue eyes alone weren't enough.

He needed something more—much more.

His mother had looked disappointed, as well she might given the trouble she had gone to. 'Nothing grand', she had said, but there had been enough crystal and Wedgwood on the endlessly long dining table to stock three antiques shops, and his father had looked predictably uncomfortable in his dinner jacket.

Daniel's thoughts meandered back to the girl in the yellow mackintosh again. For some reason she had been in the back of his mind all evening. How old? Twenty-three, he guessed, roughly the same age as her partner, or husband, or whatever he was. Not a typical beauty, not like Lucy with her wide, blue eyes and perfectly shaped nose, or any of the other girls who had crossed his path during however many years it was of bachelorhood, but there had been something about her, some indefinable quality which had arrested his attention, something strangely appealing...

Daniel yawned again, wondering vaguely about her name as he approached her cottage. No van blocking the way this time—that was something. He glanced across. The lights were still on. Was she really still working? He remembered how tired she'd looked earlier in the evening, glanced at the clock on his dashboard to confirm the time, and for some unexplainable reason brought the Land Rover to a temporary halt in the lane outside.

He thought about getting out, about walking up the garden path and knocking on the front door. But he didn't do it. If she were alone, as would seem quite likely, given that the van wasn't anywhere to be seen, she'd hardly be comfortable about letting him in to the cottage at this late hour—she didn't even know his name.

His thoughts flitted about. He felt curiously unsettled. Why did it bother him so much? Why did *she?* He found he wanted to help. There was clearly a lot of work to do in the cottage. It would surely be days before the place was properly habitable. He pictured the boy asleep in her arms, protected and warm, oblivious of the tired strain on his mother's face.

Her hair had been like fire, such a contrast to the pale face and large green eyes. What could he do for her? Maybe she was struggling at this very moment with a heavy piece of furniture, or dealing with a burst pipe.

A light flicked on in an upstairs window and she came into view. She was carrying a bucket. She didn't look tired, he decided, watching her face, just determined and purposeful.

Daniel shook his head, running a hand through his thick dark hair. He really was acting in a most peculiar manner. What on earth was he doing, lingering outside a strange woman's house late at night? He hadn't touched a drop of alcohol all evening, so it couldn't be that.

He smiled a little, gave the figure at the window one last glance, then thrust his vehicle into gear and drove away.

CHAPTER TWO

'Can I have some sweets?'

'You've only just cleaned your teeth.'

'Don't care! I want sweets!'

'What about if we feed the ducks?' Cathy bent down beside her son and pointed to the glimmer of water on the other side of the green. 'There's a pond over there, and I bet you there'll be some ducks. Look!' She held up a plastic bag. 'I've brought the crusts from breakfast.'

'Don't want to feed the stupid ducks! I don't like ducks! They're just boring, and all they do is quack. I want some sweets!'

'Robbie, please!' Cathy frowned, adjusting the bobble hat on her son's head. 'Don't be like this. Look, it's a beautiful day. Have you ever seen so many daffodils? The sun's shining, the birds are singing, and there's a horse further up the green. Shall we go and look at that?'

'No!'

Cathy stood up. She knew from bitter experience that there was little she could do when her son was in this sort of mood. He was tired, miserable and upset. She so much wanted to show Robbie everything, to share her enthusiasm for the green fields and wide open spaces, and the fresh, pure air, but if he wasn't interested then there was precious little she could do about it.

She glanced at him now, stomping along beside her, not wanting to look about or hold her hand, not wanting to do anything. Too much to expect, she supposed. It was all too new and too strange.

'What about if we spend some time feeding the ducks,

then I buy you some sweets?' Cathy suggested, after a moment. 'What about that?'

'OK.' He sounded grudging.

Cathy smiled down at his pouting face. 'Don't worry, Robbie, you will like it here eventually; I promise you,' she told him. 'It's just going to take a bit of getting used to, that's all…'

Feeding the ducks was not the picture-book success Cathy had hoped it was going to be. Robbie accepted the bag of bread she offered him, tipped the contents into the pond, then turned to her and demanded to be taken to the sweet shop.

She almost made a point of denying him his treat—if they had still been at their old home she would have done— but as it was she didn't want the day to go from bad to worse, and deep down she was afraid that Robbie was suffering and that it was all her fault.

The small shop was crammed full with every kind of provision. Cathy bought a few items for lunch, paid the amount due and handed Robbie a packet of jelly babies as promised.

'Are you interested in a raffle ticket, my dear?' The woman serving behind the counter smiled encouragingly. 'All for a good cause, and you could end up winning tickets to the Spring Ball into the bargain.'

'Oh…' Cathy smiled and quickly scanned the poster the lady was pointing to, which advertised a grand ball and a country fair to be held over the same weekend. 'I'm not sure…' She glanced into her purse. 'How much are they?'

'Three pounds each—which sounds a lot,' the woman added hurriedly, noting Cathy's expression, 'but if you win, it really is a spectacular night out. A real posh setting, with a quartet and a jazz band and some lovely food. It's held up at the manor house—such a lovely place.' The woman retrieved a book of raffle tickets from a shelf behind the counter.

'There are only a few tickets left. New to the village, aren't you?' Cathy nodded, conscious of Robbie pulling furiously on her arm. 'Well, it really would be a great way to meet all your neighbours—practically everyone from the village goes.' She placed the raffle tickets conspicuously on the counter between them. 'There aren't any tickets for the ball left to buy. So this really is the only way you'll manage to get there.'

'I'll have one.' Cathy delved into her purse for the money. After all, she reasoned, three pounds wasn't that much money—not these days—and buying a raffle ticket would sort of mark her entrance into the village. Besides, with Robbie threatening to play up she was more than anxious to be out of the shop.

'That's lovely!' The woman, pleased with her sale, took Cathy's money from her and wrote down her details on the ticket stub. 'They always let me have a few pairs of tickets up at the house. I do a bit for the local old people; the proceeds from this will go towards their summer outing. Look after this raffle ticket, now!' she called, as Cathy opened the door and a stream of sunshine flooded into the rather gloomy interior. 'We'll need that for proof of purchase if you win.'

Fat chance of that! Cathy thought as she left the shop. When have I ever won anything in my life before?

'Cathy? Cathy Taylor, is that you?' Cathy turned around, surprised that someone should be calling her by name. A young woman, about her own age, was walking towards her. 'It *is* you! Goodness gracious! Well, you are the last person I expected to see here!' The neat coral mouth curved into an attractive smile. 'You're looking well!'

'Am I?' Cathy smiled too, stalling for time.

'Now, be honest, you haven't a clue who I am, have you?' The young woman laughed gaily. 'I can see it in your expression!'

'Well, no…' Cathy smiled hesitantly. She glanced at the

glamorous apparition before her, scanning her memory for possibilities.

'Don't worry, I'm not offended. In fact I think it would be worse if you *did* recognise me—I used to look dreadful at school. Fat with glasses and my hair in a frightful mess!'

The picture began to be a bit clearer. Cathy focused on the beautifully made-up face more closely. 'Sandra?' she queried. 'Sandra Beale? We used to sit together in Maths.'

'You've got it! So, how are you after all these years?'

'Oh, I'm fine.' Cathy managed a weak smile. She felt rather overwhelmed. It was difficult to take in that this gorgeous-looking woman was the same quiet, frumpy girl that no one had bothered much with at school.

'I know what you're thinking.' Even white teeth flashed becomingly in the sunlight. 'Such a metamorphosis, isn't it?' Sandra spread her arms wide, showing off herself to full effect. She was dressed elegantly in shades of cream and brown. Cathy's gaze rested appreciatively on fitted jodphurs and a beautifully soft roll-neck pullover, worn beneath a chunky brown corduroy jacket. On her feet were a pair of supple, knee-length leather boots.

'What happened?' Cathy asked, trying not to imagine the sort of mess she must look in comparison. She had bathed in four inches of lukewarm water this morning, thrown on a pair of clean, but rather worn denims, and grabbed the nearest jumper to hand from the large cardboard box that was part of her wardrobe. It happened to be a dazzling assortment of multicoloured stripes and extremely large. Cathy pushed the sleeves up over her hands. With a purple woollen hat jammed on her bubbly red hair, she felt like a clown in comparison to Sandra's tastefully clad figure.

'Oh, I decided I was sick of being Little Miss Nobody. Amazing what you can do with a bottle of bleach, contact lenses, make-up and a few well-chosen clothes, isn't it?'

'You look…' Cathy shook her head in admiration. 'Stunning.'

'Thanks!' Sandra looked suitably pleased. 'So what are you doing here? Visiting?'

'Er...no. No, actually, I've...well, we've just moved in.'

'Really?' Sandra didn't bother to hide her surprise. 'Where?'

'Stanway Cottage. It's just past the last turning to the green, next to the tree which looks as if its about to fall down.'

'You don't mean old Mrs Payne's place?'

'Yes.' Cathy tilted her chin slightly. There was a distinct note of incredulity in Sandra's tone.

'Good gracious. Have you bought it?'

'No. I just rent.'

'Oh, I see. She's in a home now, isn't she? I suppose her family are just biding their time.'

Cathy nodded. 'Something like that.'

'You said *we*,' Sandra commented purposefully. 'Are you married?'

'Yes—umm, I mean, no. No, I'm not married, but I'm with someone.' Cathy turned towards Robbie, who was engrossed in biting the heads off all the red jelly babies. 'This is my son. Robbie...' Cathy touched him on the shoulder. 'Say hello to Sandra, Robbie. We used to go to school together.'

'Hello.' He looked up briefly, gave a formidable scowl, and then focused his concentration back on his packet of sweets.

'He's not usually as antisocial as this,' Cathy explained. 'But he's a bit tired. We only moved in last night.'

'Oh, he's adorable!' Sandra's smile was bright—maybe just a little too bright, Cathy thought as she glanced at her fixed expression. 'How old is he?'

'Five. He'll be six in a few weeks' time.'

There was a slight hesitation. 'So...it's just the two of you, is it?'

Cathy nodded. 'Yes, that's right. What about you?' she asked swiftly. 'Do you live around here?'

'Yes. Someone I used to...er...know died and left me his little place. He was a friend of the family.'

'Lucky you.' Cathy smiled. 'I have no connections here whatsoever. I know it's only a few miles out of town, but it might just as well be on the other side of the world. I remember visiting once on a school field trip, and then when I saw the advert in the local paper—' Cathy stopped babbling. It was clear she no longer had Sandra's full attention anyway.

'I want to go!' Robbie sounded bored.

'Yes, in a minute, sweetheart.' Cathy turned and followed Sandra's gaze, curious to know what it was that had her so completely transfixed.

She couldn't see anything out of the ordinary, just the green and the trees and the narrow path which wound its way to the village store. There was an old lady on a bike with an empty shopping bag hooked over the handlebars, a young girl skipping alongside a mother with a pushchair, and a man walking alone. Actually, something about him looked vaguely familiar. Cathy looked more closely and her heart skipped a sudden, unexpected beat.

'I want to go!' Robbie had finished his sweets and was tugging impatiently on Cathy's hand. 'Stop talking!'

'*Robbie!*' Cathy frowned down at her son. 'Don't be so rude.'

'I want to go!' He pulled free from Cathy's grasp.

'Perhaps you'd like to call by some time,' she suggested, but Sandra wasn't listening. Cathy looked across and saw that the object of her desire was rapidly approaching. 'Well, I must be getting back,' she announced after a moment. 'Come on, Robbie, let's go and see that horse—*Robbie?*'

Cathy spun around wildly. She couldn't see him. She scanned the area in front of the village store, the green, the duck pond where they had fed the ducks...

'Oh no!' Cathy dropped her bag of shopping and broke

into a run. *'Robbie!'* she cried. 'Don't go any closer! Robbie!'

He was at the water's edge, stepping off the path and treading carefully down the side of the bank. There had been a lot of rain last night, so it would be very slippery. Cathy ran towards him as fast as she could, wondering how he had got away from her so quickly.

There was a cry, and she watched as he fell, sliding down the bank with a whoosh and ending up in the water. Cathy ran faster, aware out of the corner of her eye of other movement from the far side of the green.

He was crying when she got to him. He had managed to get to his feet, but he was standing in about six inches of water and looking very miserable and frightened. 'Robbie!' Cathy held out her hand and tried to sound calm, despite her thudding heart. 'Come on. Take my hand.'

'I can't!'

'I'm not cross with you.' She very carefully placed her feet at the edge of the water. 'Come on, sweetheart.' He was sinking. Cathy stared in horror as the top of his wellington boots began to let in water. 'Robbie, stay still!' she instructed. 'I'm coming to get you!'

Cathy stepped in. The water was cold and sludgy, but she didn't care. She stretched forward and lifted Robbie out of the pond. It was a struggle, and for one awful moment, she thought she was going to fall, but after a distinctly wobbly moment she managed it.

'Sandra, will you take him from me? I think *I'm* stuck now.' Cathy held Robbie out towards Sandra, who was standing at the edge of the bank. *'Sandra?'* she repeated, feeling the ache in her muscles as she struggled to hold Robbie clear of the water and keep herself in an upright position.

'I don't think I can reach.' Sandra made a tiny movement and gingerly ventured near to the water. 'My boots...' she murmured. 'They're brand-new. Can't you come a bit closer?'

'No!' Cathy inhaled a breath. 'For goodness' sake—!'

'It's OK. I'll take him from you.'

Cathy glanced to her right and saw the man from the previous evening. Oblivious of the fact that his boots were ankle-deep in mud, he took Robbie from her aching grasp.

'Oh, thank you!' Cathy had never felt so relieved to see someone take her son from her. Her arms were aching madly, and, as she had suspected, she was now stuck fast.

'Wait a moment and I'll come back for you.' The man set a tearful Robbie down on the path and ruffled his hair. 'Don't cry,' he told him gently. 'You're out now.'

'But what about Mummy—?'

Cathy frowned as Robbie began to cry in earnest. 'I'm all right, darling!' she called. 'Just a bit stuck, that's all.' She tried to look cheerful, wondering at the same time how in the world they had managed to get themselves in such a pickle.

'Can you move at all?'

Cathy struggled to lift a leg. 'No,' she replied flatly. A crowd had begun to gather now. Cathy had never felt more ridiculous in the whole of her life. She looked across at Robbie and managed a cheerful smile, which she hoped masked some of the embarrassment she was feeling.

'Don't cry, champ!' The man crouched down in front of Robbie, who was becoming more and more upset. 'Mummy will be out in a flash.'

'You're going to ruin your clothes,' Cathy warned, feeling incredibly foolish as her rescuer began wading out towards her.

'They'll wash,' he responded, with a reassuring smile. 'Don't worry about it. Now take my hand...'

He had a long reach, and a sureness of foot that Cathy wished she possessed. She placed her hand in his, felt the strength of his fingers as they closed around hers and in a moment she was free and being hauled away from the muddy water.

He really was akin to a knight in shining armour, Cathy

thought afterwards, when she and Robbie were safely standing on dry land again. Twice now he had come to her aid…

'OK now?'

He had the most glorious smile. Cathy inhaled a ragged breath and nodded. 'Yes. Thank you. Thank you very much,' she repeated. 'I don't know what we would have done without you. I'm so sorry we've put you to this much trouble. What with getting so wet last night and now this…' She glanced down at his sodden boots and mud-splattered denims. 'You have ruined your clothes,' she murmured. 'I'm so sorry—'

'There really is no need to keep apologising. Think nothing of it. I'm glad I was around to be of assistance.' Cathy looked into his face and felt a sharp, delicious pang as his eyes sparkled good-humouredly. 'It's certainly livened up this Saturday morning, and one thing is for sure: you won't forget your first morning in Langforde.'

Cathy grew warm beneath her striped clown jumper. He was *so* handsome: dark, dark eyes, long spiky lashes, an angular jaw, and a mouth that revealed so much good humour it made her want to smile just looking at him.

He was dressed perfectly too. Definitely an outdoor type, Cathy thought: rugged and strong-looking, clad in the denims and a worn leather jacket with a plaid scarf wrapped casually around his neck.

'Do you two *know* each other?' Sandra, who had been looking disgruntled by the whole episode, piped up suddenly.

'Yes. Well, sort of…' Cathy smiled brightly, conscious of the flush of heat still rising from her neck.

'I helped Cathy and her friend move a few things into her cottage.'

'Oh! I see.' There was a pause whilst Sandra assimilated this information.

'Well, Robbie and I had better be getting back!' Cathy

announced. 'Oh!' She glanced over towards the village shop. 'My shopping.'

'I'll get that for you.' Sandra, clearly feeling the need to show she wasn't totally useless, hurried over towards Cathy's things.

'Well!' Cathy looked up into wonderful dark eyes and struggled to think of something vaguely sensible to say. 'Robbie seems none the worse for his adventure!' She looked down at her son, who had stopped crying and was now standing in his muddy socks, tipping the water out of his wellington boots. 'I don't know your name,' she added suddenly. 'I'm Cathy,' she said hurriedly, conscious that she had spoken without thinking, 'and this is Robbie.'

'Daniel.' His gaze was steady and direct. He held out his hand and smiled. 'Very pleased to meet you.'

'Likewise.' Cathy shook his outstretched hand. His grip was firm and reassuring, and managed to do strange things to her insides. His voice, she thought. That was another thing which just made her want to melt. She glanced across at Sandra and saw that she was approaching with her shopping. 'She's very attractive, isn't she?'

He looked briefly. 'Yes. Very.'

Why had she said that? Talk about emphasising the differences between them! Cathy speculated on her own ragged appearance and cursed silently. Was she mad?

'Thanks!' Cathy took the shopping from Sandra and checked inside the bags to make sure her purse was still there. It had all the money she possessed in the world, which wasn't much, but if she lost that... The words 'destitute' and 'disaster' sprang to mind.

'I'll walk back with you.'

'Oh, surely there's no need for that!' Sandra's voice sounded a little strained. 'I mean,' she added, glancing apologetically in Daniel's direction, 'I could give you both a lift in my car.'

'That's very nice of you.' Cathy smiled gratefully. 'But we're very grubby. I wouldn't want to ruin the interior, and besides, you'd have to go and get it and…' She shook her head decisively.

'Sandra doesn't live too far from the shop,' Daniel explained. 'I'm sure it wouldn't be that much trouble.'

'Well, actually…' Sandra looked a little anxious now, presumably at the prospect of her car being used as a taxi for two not very clean individuals. 'I am just about to go out.'

'That's settled, then!' Cathy didn't want to accept help from anyone who wasn't happy about giving it. 'We'll walk. Robbie and I will be perfectly all right. It's just a little water and mud.' Cathy glanced down at her legs. 'Well, perhaps a lot of water and mud,' she added lightly. 'Either way, it's not going to harm us to walk home.'

'In that case you will have me as a companion.'

Cathy looked into Daniel's face and recognised the expression of someone who could be as stubborn and determined as she was. He took the bags of shopping from her grasp. 'Maybe Robbie would like a shoulder-ride? His feet might get quite sore in those boots.'

'Yes! Yes!' Robbie brightened up immediately. 'Can I, Mummy? Please?' He wrapped his arms around her legs. 'I'm sorry I went in the pond. Can I have a ride up high?'

'Well…' Cathy frowned across at Daniel. 'You'll get even dirtier.'

'I think I'm going to need a shower anyway—a bit more mud won't make much difference.'

The walk back to the cottage felt almost surreal—as far as Cathy was concerned anyway. It was like… She hesitated, not wanting to use such a word, even in the privacy of her own mind. Silly. When had 'family' ever meant anything other than Robbie and herself? She glanced up at Daniel, who was in deep conversation with her suddenly very chatty son, and inhaled a steadying breath.

No wonder Sandra was smitten—what girl wouldn't be? Cathy visualised Sandra's crestfallen expression as Daniel had announced his intention to walk her and Robbie home and wondered how close Daniel and she were.

They arrived back at the cottage far too quickly. Daniel lowered Robbie gently to his feet and waited whilst Cathy unlocked the front door. 'You've been very kind.' She took the shopping bags which Daniel held out to her and smiled. 'Thank you.'

'My pleasure.' He couldn't keep from looking into her face. She was so…not beautiful exactly, but arresting. So different, with her pale, pale face and crazy red hair and the most gorgeous green eyes Daniel had ever seen. He thought frantically for something sensible to say. 'If you ever need anything else…' He smiled, conscious of his own inadequacies, which was strange because usually he had no trouble talking to women. No trouble at all…

'I hope there won't be any more calamities! Although with Robbie around anything can happen!' She grinned. 'He looks so angelic too—don't you, scamp?'

'He's great.' Daniel gazed at the small boy, who was now on his hands and knees watching intently as a bumble bee buzzed its way in and out of some daffodils which were struggling through the undergrowth near to the front door. 'Is Robbie starting school on Monday?'

'Yes.'

There was a pause.

'Are you alone here?'

'*Alone?*'

He saw her frown and realised the stupidity of his remark, but decided to persevere anyway. 'You have Robbie, of course, but—'

'It's not really any of your business, is it?' She reddened as she spoke, but she looked fierce suddenly, and somehow more vulnerable than ever.

'I didn't mean…' He inhaled a steadying breath. 'I didn't mean to pry,' he finished. He raised his hand in a gesture of apology. 'Sorry. You're right. It is none of my business—'

'No!' Cathy released a breath as he began to turn away. 'Please, it's me who should be apologising. I'm sorry, I didn't mean to snap. Thank you...for what you did. I...' Her voice trailed away. 'Thank you,' she repeated anxiously.

'Well, you two need to get cleaned up.' He saw at once that she felt awkward, and that it would be better if he departed. 'I'll no doubt see you around the village.'

'Yes...I...expect so.'

She hadn't said 'hope'. I hope so. He knew he was being ridiculous. What did it matter?

Daniel smiled briefly, said goodbye to Robbie, then turned away from the dilapidated cottage, conscious that something strange was happening to him.

He thought about her for the rest of the day, picturing snapshots in his mind: the way she had looked, stranded in the mud with her son in her arms, her smile, the vulnerability of her expression on that first evening at the cottage when she had looked so tired and somehow strangely alone. Her expression in that last moment of seeing her, almost as if she had wanted to cry...

He dwelt on the image long into the night. He accepted an invitation from friends and found himself thinking about her between lulls in the conversation. One of the group, a beautiful woman, a friend of a friend whom he saw from time to time, even commented on his lack of attention when they were sitting around the dining table in the expensive restaurant on the green. 'You look thoughtful,' she murmured playfully as she sipped her coffee. 'Something on your mind?'

'Not something, some*one*!' Joe, another old friend, who had drunk too much wine and had a house almost opposite on the far side of the green, grinned inanely. 'I saw you this morning! Playing Sir Galahad to that colourful woman with the little boy!' He turned to the others assembled around the circular table. 'Honestly, it was a picture to warm the cockles of your heart! Mind you, Sandra the Sexpot didn't look too pleased to be left on her own!'

'You could be in serious trouble, Daniel!' someone else remarked laughingly. 'She won't chase after you any more.'

'Oh, I think he's safe enough,' Joe continued. 'From what I gather she's just as determined as ever she was.'

'Shut up, Joe, and drink some more coffee!' Daniel's voice revealed an uncharacteristic edge of anger. He rose to his feet, conscious of the surprised looks from around the table. 'It's been a long day. I think I'll have an early night.' He glanced down at the woman at his side. 'Do you want me to take you home?'

He saw her expression and knew she had expected a rather different ending to the evening. 'No, it's all right,' she replied stiffly. 'It's too early yet. I'll get a taxi.'

He took the long way round, avoiding her cottage. The detour would add several minutes to his journey, but what did that matter? The fresh air would help to clear his head anyway.

He wondered what she would be doing on this Saturday night. Cleaning again? He hoped not. He pictured her hands, remembering the short, unvarnished nails and faintly callused palms. There had been no ring. Did that mean...? Not necessarily. Daniel pictured the man with his short jacket and tattooed hands and found that he didn't want to believe that they were together.

Cathy had just put Robbie to bed when the doorbell rang. It made her start. She stood for a moment in the kitchen, wondering who it might be, half hoping that it was Daniel, so that she could apologise. She had acted so ungratefully. She really didn't know what had come over her. Cathy ran a shaky hand through her hair and walked towards the front door.

'Sandra...!' She told herself she was foolish to feel so disappointed.

'Hello, Cathy! I was passing and I saw the light...' Sandra glanced beyond Cathy into the hallway. 'Are you busy?'

'Er...no.' Cathy pictured the mess in every room. 'Come on in!' She held the door open wide and Sandra walked past her into the gloomy hall. She looked so out of place, dressed as she was in an immaculate navy blue dress and strappy shoes, that Cathy was moved to warn her not to get too close to the walls. 'I haven't had a chance to clean everywhere yet,' she explained. 'They're probably not too bad, but your dress looks very expensive and I wouldn't want you to ruin it on my account.'

Sandra's smile as she made her way through into the living room changed to one of undisguised horror. It's not that bad! Cathy thought irritably. She glanced around the kitchen, which she had scrubbed clean. OK, so it was a bit tatty, but even so...

'How did you get on, after your little escapade this morning?' Sandra examined a chair carefully before she sat down. 'No lasting damage, I hope?'

Cathy smiled. 'None at all! In fact I think Robbie's rather pleased with himself—he's turned it into some kind of adventure. Would you like some tea?'

'Umm...no, thank you. I can't stay long; I'm on my way somewhere.'

'You look very nice,' Cathy remarked sincerely. 'I love your dress.'

Sandra glanced down at herself. 'Thanks.' She hesitated. 'So...did Daniel stay long this morning, after he'd walked you and Robbie home?'

Ah! Cathy thought. Now they were at the crux of the matter. She glanced across at Sandra's deliberately indifferent expression and knew it would be cruel to tell her anything other than the truth. 'No, he didn't even come inside.'

'Oh!' The relief on Sandra's face was clear for all to see.

'He's very handsome, isn't he?' Cathy remarked in conversational tones.

'Yes.'

'Is he married?'

'No.' Sandra shook her head decisively. 'I don't think he's ever come remotely close.'

'But he must have a girlfriend.' Cathy smiled. 'I would have thought he'd be snapped up straight away.'

'Not at the moment—at least nothing serious. And that's the main thing, isn't it?' Sandra glanced across at Cathy and added, somewhat pointedly. 'Of course, like all men, he's more than happy to have a fling with someone, but when it comes to anything long-term he's incredibly choosy. He wouldn't get seriously involved with anyone who didn't match up to his high standards.'

'Really?' Cathy didn't bother to hide her amusement. 'You seem very knowledgeable on the subject.' She decided to get straight to the point. 'Have you and he...?'

'No.' Sandra's voice was undeniably flat. 'No,' she repeated, with a little more vigour. 'Unfortunately not. However, I live in hope.'

'He's extremely good with children,' Cathy commented, more for something to say than anything else. 'Robbie took to him straight away. I've never seen him so chatty with such a comparative stranger.'

'Yes...well, he's very...' Sandra struggled to come up with the right word. 'Amenable,' she said finally. 'Always willing to help those in need.'

Meaning me, Cathy thought.

Sandra glanced at her wristwatch. 'Well, this was just a flying visit; I really must be going. I'm meeting someone for dinner—not a patch on the delicious Daniel, of course, but I never like to refuse an invitation, especially if it means a free meal into the bargain!'

Cathy made no comment. She began to see that Sandra's

reincarnation from frumpy schoolgirl to glamorous siren had not been the complete success she had first imagined.

At the front door, Sandra paused briefly. 'Daniel's a very *kind* person,' she reiterated. 'And of course there's the rebel element to consider as well.'

Cathy wasn't quite sure what she was talking about, but she smiled and said cheerfully, 'Quite a combination, I should think!'

'Exactly. But it's just as well to be aware of these things from the beginning. There really is nothing worse than making a fool of yourself over a man, is there?'

And with that rather ironic comment hanging in the air between them, Sandra walked out into the night.

CHAPTER THREE

CATHY glanced at her wristwatch for the tenth time in as many minutes and sighed with relief. At last, time to collect Robbie from school!

It was glorious to be out in the fresh air after working inside all day. Cathy breathed in deeply as she strolled along the lane towards the village school. The hedgerows were bursting with fresh green life. The sky was a clear, sharp blue. Daffodils scattered along the grassy verge added drifts of vivid yellow to a scene that, in Cathy's opinion, couldn't be more perfect. She walked with a smile on her face. She just couldn't help it. To be here, on a day like this...

The mellow stone of the village school came into view and her heart soared a little more. She missed Robbie such a lot when he was at school, more especially at the moment because she knew that he wasn't particularly happy.

There were several mothers already waiting for their children at the school gates. Cathy smiled at a couple of familiar faces and received a few friendly greetings in return.

She had timed it perfectly; a child emerged from the front door and rang a handbell with vigorous enthusiasm and in less than a minute children of all sizes streamed out into the playground.

Cathy waited expectantly for Robbie's sweet little face to appear. Each day this week had been torturous. Robbie had cried and wailed at the school gates every morning before school, clinging onto her legs, pleading with her not to make him go... Tears welled up in Cathy's eyes at the thought of it. She had felt *so* mean. Guilty, too, at taking

34

him away from his old school. Anxious in case things would never get better.

After five minutes, the frenetic activity at the gate quietened down as mothers and children left for home. Cathy stood alone, her eyes glued to the front entrance, waiting for Robbie. She felt uneasy; he was usually one of the first to come running out.

She was just about to go inside the school and find him for herself when she caught sight of him. Her heart sank, for all the signs told her that something was wrong. Why else would he be walking across the playground with the formidable Miss Stubbs at his side?

'Mummy! Mummy!' Robbie ran towards her, arms outstretched, like a prisoner released from jail.

'Hello, darling!' Cathy bent down and swung Robbie into the air. 'How's my best boy?' She kissed his smooth, plump cheek and gave him a quick, fierce hug, conscious of their shared emotion at being reunited with each other again. 'Are you OK?'

'S'pose.' Robbie glanced briefly across at Miss Stubbs, and then buried his head against Cathy's shoulder. 'Can we go home now?' he mumbled.

'I need to speak to you for a few moments, Miss Taylor, if you don't mind.'

Cathy's stomach churned over. The elderly woman didn't look particularly happy; her lips were pursed into a thin, hard line of disapproval. 'Er…yes. Yes, of course.' She inhaled a breath. 'Is there…something the matter?'

'I think it would be best if we talked inside. I don't believe in discussing important matters out on the school yard.'

Oh, dear! Was it *that* serious, then? 'Robbie, I just need to have a quick word with Miss Stubbs.' Cathy's expression was deliberately upbeat, even though she felt a certain amount of trepidation inside. 'I'm sure it won't take long and then we can go home.'

'But, Mummy,' Robbie lifted his head and looked earnestly into his mother's eyes. 'I'm not a naughty boy; I'm not! I didn't mean to spill the paint, or make the book corner all messy!'

'Robbie, shh!' Cathy held her son close and followed Miss Stubbs across the playground, towards the school building. 'Calm down, darling,' she whispered. 'I'm sure you haven't done anything wrong. Miss Stubbs just wants to have a chat, that's all.'

The school was oddly quiet now that the children had left for home. 'Perhaps, Robbie, you would like to play over in the corner with the sand whilst I talk with your mother,' Miss Stubbs suggested once they were in the classroom.

'Go on, darling,' Cathy urged, when Robbie stubbornly made no move. 'Just for a few minutes.'

'Now that's an example of what I want to talk to you about, Miss Taylor,' the teacher asserted, once Robbie was out of earshot. 'I've had an extremely difficult time with your son this week.'

'I see.' Cathy inhaled a steadying breath. 'Well, I know he's upset each morning—' she began.

'There's more to it than that!' There was an edge to the teacher's voice which couldn't be ignored. 'I'm sorry to have to say this, but your son is incredibly disobedient, and it's having a disruptive effect on the rest of my class!'

'Oh!' Cathy stood open-mouthed for a moment. She didn't have a clue what to say. 'I know he's having a little difficulty in adjusting,' she murmured. 'Robbie had just got settled at his last school and then we came here...'

'Not exactly the best of times for a move!' Miss Stubbs replied disapprovingly. 'But I think we need to look deeper than that,' she continued. 'I get the impression that he's not used to a great amount of discipline at home.'

'Discipline?' Cathy glanced across to where Robbie was playing in the sand. He looked so sweet and adorable, with his hair ruffled and the bobble hat on his head all askew.

'I...' Cathy floundered for a suitable reply. 'He's not actually very naughty at home.'

'It's just you, isn't it?'

Cathy frowned. 'What is?' she queried, wishing Robbie still had his previous class teacher, a wonderfully warm, cheerful young woman, who had seemed to find him no trouble at all.

'Robbie's father isn't around.'

Cathy hardened her voice, forcing herself to look Miss Stubbs straight in the eye. 'No, he's not, but I don't honestly see what that has to do with anything!'

'Well, I think that last point is debatable,' Miss Stubbs continued, with a distinct air of superiority. A smile crept across the lined mouth. 'I see it time and again, Miss Taylor. I try to teach discipline, a certain set of values, and my work is eroded because of lack of support in the home. I'm sure you are trying to do your best,' she added briskly, before Cathy could reply, 'but boys need a firm hand. Of course we don't have many single families,' she commented, 'not in this village.' She walked across to her desk and picked up a file. 'You came from a rather difficult area of town, I understand?'

'I don't see what that has to do with anything!' Cathy interjected. 'Robbie was incredibly happy at his last school.'

'Yes, so you keep saying. Well, I suppose the change in environment will be having an effect,' Miss Stubbs continued. 'Although I can't say that Robbie's showing much appreciation of all this wonderful countryside. He drew a picture of his old block of flats today, when I specifically asked for a drawing of something in the village.'

'He misses his old home. Isn't that understandable?' Cathy replied, in a choked voice. 'For goodness' sake Miss Stubbs, he's only five—!'

'Miss Stubbs, I'm looking for my other holdall. Did I leave it in here by any—?'

Cathy spun around at the sound of the deep, familiar

voice. For a split second she told herself wishful thinking had imagined him here, but, no, there Daniel was, looking as stunningly handsome as ever, his large, rugged frame practically filling the doorway of the classroom.

'My apologies. I had no idea you had someone with you—*Cathy*?' His smile was warm as he recognised her. 'Hello! How are you?' His dark eyes flicked from Cathy's strained expression to Miss Stubbs's upright figure, then back again. His brow creased slightly as he registered the tense atmosphere. 'Is everything OK?'

'Miss Taylor and I are just having a little chat about Robbie,' Miss Stubbs replied, in surprisingly smooth honeyed tones. 'Nothing to worry about, I'm sure. You're looking for your holdall, you say?' Beady eyes scanned the room. 'There it is, over by my desk.'

'Ah, yes. Thanks.' Daniel, dressed as usual in well-fitting worn denims and a simple white tee-shirt, which did much to emphasise the athletic strength of his body, entered the classroom and picked it up. 'Sorry for the interruption.'

'That's quite all right.' Miss Stubbs was all smiles—until she noticed Robbie's exploits with the sand. 'Robbie, for goodness' sake, just look at the mess you're making!' she snapped.

Cathy knew she couldn't stay here a moment longer. 'Robbie, come on. Let's go home.'

'But, Miss Taylor, we haven't finished our little chat.'

'Actually, Miss Stubbs, I think you've said all there is to say.' Cathy's voice wobbled a little, but she worked hard and managed to hide the fact that all she wanted to do in that moment was burst into tears. 'Robbie's tired and so am I—it's been a long, hard week.' She strode over to the sandpit in the corner of the classroom and held out her hand. 'Come on, sweetheart, dust yourself down.'

'Miss Taylor! I really don't think we've come to a satisfactory conclusion. We really do need to discuss this further—'

'What? The fact that I'm a single parent and you don't

approve?' Cathy eyed the sour woman with dislike, conscious that Daniel's presence was enabling her to be far more assertive than she otherwise would have dared. 'Well, I'm afraid there's nothing I can do about that, Miss Stubbs. I bring Robbie up the best way I know how, and all I can tell you is he's a perfectly reasonable child when he's with me.' Cathy placed a protective hand on her son's shoulder. 'He's been extremely unhappy all week and it's been torture—for both of us.' Her voice shook noticeably 'Now, if you'll excuse me, all I want to do is to go home.'

'Miss Taylor—!'

Cathy didn't wait to hear any more. Daniel stood aside and she exited the classroom without so much as a backward glance, conscious of the anger and misery bubbling up inside.

Poor Robbie! The thought that he had endured so many hours in that woman's company—! Cathy ran a shaky hand through her hair. Miss Stubbs didn't even look as if she liked children! Cathy closed her eyes. Perhaps this was all a mistake. How could she have imagined that she could just up sticks and move to a place like this without there being huge consequences?

She crouched down in the corridor and placed a gentle palm against Robbie's cheek. 'Have you been a naughty boy today?'

'No…'

Cathy knew that look. 'Not even a little bit?' she asked gently.

'P'raps…just a bit.' Robbie hung his head. 'We have to sit still all the time, and we can't talk, and…' His voice trailed to a halt. Robbie looked towards the closed classroom door. 'She's not nice! Why can't she be all smiley and funny like Miss Collins was?'

'I don't know.' Cathy heaved a sigh and rose to her feet. She heard a murmur of voices from behind the classroom door and wondered what Daniel and Miss Stubbs were talking about.

'Is Daniel telling Miss Stubbs off?' Robbie asked hope-fully. 'For being so *mean*,' he added, with feeling. 'He taught us painting today. He's very funny. We did about buildings.' Robbie grabbed Cathy's hand. 'I'll show you mine, if you like. Daniel said it was very good.'

'I promise I'll look at it first thing on Monday. Only, I don't think it's such a good idea to go in there now.'

'You can't on Monday. Nor Tuesday,' Robbie told her gleefully. 'We've got holidays…' He thrust a small fist into the pocket of his trousers and produced a screwed-up piece of paper. 'It says on this letter Miss Stubbs gave to us.'

'Oh.' Cathy smoothed out the paper and read the con-tents quickly. The school, it seemed, was having to have some emergency work done on its roof. 'Well, that's nice, then, isn't it?' She beamed down at Robbie. 'A lovely long weekend together.' Cathy glanced regretfully towards the classroom door, half hoping Daniel would appear. 'Well, I suppose we'd better be going.' She took Robbie's hand. 'Come on, scamp!' she added cheerfully. 'Let's see what we can have for tea.'

'Cathy! Wait up!' After a few moments, Daniel's deep voice echoed down the empty corridor.

Cathy inhaled a steadying breath, turning to watch as he caught up with her. She really needed to conquer this feel-ing of light-headed excitement, she told herself. It surely couldn't be the best thing for her heart.

'Are you OK?'

'As well as can be expected.' She managed a weak smile, conscious of the thudding inside her chest. 'Considering I've just been told I'm inadequate as a parent, that is.'

'She said that to you?' His dark head shook. 'Don't let Miss Stubbs upset you. She's not the greatest diplomat in the world. And it's Friday; she's tired.'

'You're making excuses for her!' Cathy accused.

'No.' Daniel's voice was firm. 'No, I promise you, I'm not.' His mouth curved into a warm, sympathetic smile. 'I'm just trying to make you feel better.'

Cathy shook her head a little and frowned. 'I'm not sure she even *likes* children!' she murmured, squeezing Robbie's plump hand. She glanced up into Daniel's face, conscious of how desperately glad she was to see him again. 'Do you think I was *very* rude?'

'Do you care?' Dark eyes sparkled mischievously. Heavens! Cathy thought, as her stomach turned an unexpected somersault. No wonder Sandra is desperate to get her hands on him. 'No,' Daniel added. 'I thought you were…' He hesitated a moment. 'Just right.'

'Really?' Cathy frowned, wondered what was going through his mind. 'I hate confrontation,' she declared. 'Look at me!' She held out her hand. 'I'm shaking like a leaf!'

'I'll give you a lift home.' Daniel's fingers were strong and firm. The thrill of his touch was like an electric shock. She stared down as he squeezed her hand reassuringly, cursing the fact that kindness always made her want to cry. 'You'll be fine. Hey!' Daniel's voice was gentle. He squeezed her hand again, bending his six-foot-plus frame a little, tilting Cathy's chin so that he could look into her face, frowning as he saw the tears. 'Hey, now. You know she's not worth it,' he asserted gently. 'She's old and crotchety and a snob to boot.'

'You're right.' Cathy sniffed and wiped away the tears with the back of her hand. 'I know you're right. It's just…well, it's been a hard week, and now this—' She inhaled a huge breath, conscious of a small, anxious face looking up at her.

'Mummy, don't cry!' Robbie's small voice wavered a little. He tugged at her hand. 'Please!'

Daniel delved into the pocket of his trousers and produced a handkerchief. Then he bent down and scooped Robbie into his arms. 'How about a ride home in my Land Rover?'

'Yeah!' Robbie jiggled excitedly. 'I want to go in the Land Rover! I want to go in the Land Rover!'

Cathy smiled, curious now to know what Daniel was doing here. 'Are you a teacher?' she asked.

'A teacher?' The gorgeous mouth curved a little. 'Absolutely not! One day a week is enough for me.'

They began walking along the corridor towards the main entrance of the school. 'I just help out,' he continued conversationally. 'The school needed someone to help with art, so…' Broad shoulders were lifted in a shrug. 'I offered.'

'That's very good of you—you don't get paid, I take it?'

'No.' Daniel held open the main door for Cathy and Robbie and they emerged into the fresh spring air. 'I do it for the love of working with people like Miss Stubbs,' he added dryly.

'Careful!' Cathy whispered urgently, staring into a space behind Daniel's left shoulder. She watched as he glanced around quickly. 'Got you!' She grinned, glad of the opportunity to lighten the atmosphere. 'All this talk about taking no notice of what Miss Stubbs says,' she accused. 'You're as frightened of her as I am!'

Daniel held up both hands in supplication. 'OK, I admit it. She terrifies the life out of me!' His mouth twisted humorously. 'That was cruel!' he asserted. 'For a split second I actually thought she was standing right behind me! My heart is banging away like a steam train.' On impulse he took Cathy's hand in his. 'Here, feel it!'

Touching him caused turmoil. Cathy felt the solid strength of his chest beneath her splayed fingers, the touch of his hand upon hers, and struggled to blot out the sharp ache of desire which surged through her body. *His* heart was beating fast? Cathy tried to keep a calm façade. She hadn't expected this. Not Miss Stubbs, nor her outburst, but most especially not Daniel. It was difficult keeping her thoughts under control when he was near. He was so… She shook her head, hardly able to put what she thought about him into words. Kind…handsome…funny…utterly irresistible…

'You see what you've done to me?' Dark, mesmeric eyes held Cathy's gaze.

'Sorry…' she murmured.

'Don't apologise.' His expression was unexpectedly serious suddenly. 'I think I can live with it…'

'Mummy!' Cathy felt a tug on her jumper. She dropped her hand like a stone and looked down at her son. *'Come on!'* he pleaded impatiently. 'I want a ride in the Land Rover!'

'You're sure this is no trouble?' Cathy asked, once they were standing beside the rather tatty vehicle in the small school car park.

'If it was, I wouldn't have offered,' Daniel replied easily. 'Wait a minute. It sticks like hell.' He walked around to the passenger side of the Land Rover and tugged open the door. 'Another thing I keep meaning to have seen to,' he commented, with a rueful smile. 'There's a whole *list* of things.' He picked Robbie up and swung him onto the passenger seat, then stood aside to allow Cathy to clamber up. 'You know how it is.'

'Oh, don't I just!' Cathy remarked forcibly. She released a sigh, thinking about the effort she had to put in just to save a pound here and a penny there. 'Isn't money the most annoying thing in the world?' She smiled. 'Particularly when you haven't got any! How do you manage?' she added. 'Giving up one of your days a week here is pretty generous.'

'Oh, I get by. I've got a fair amount of time on my hands, so—'

'You're unemployed?'

A slight frown creased Daniel's forehead and Cathy blushed scarlet. 'Sorry! I didn't mean to pry—' She shook her head, mentally cursing her runaway mouth.

'Unemployed?' She saw the look of puzzlement and then his brow cleared. 'No. No, I'm not.' He smiled. 'Although some might say… No, I paint.' He inserted the key into the ignition and started the engine. 'Or at least that's the general idea.'

'Walls? Windowsills?' Cathy queried.

Daniel's mouth twisted into a smile. 'Watercolours,' he replied. 'And oils.'

'You're a proper artist?' Cathy's mouth widened into a smile. 'Oh, that's marvellous!' she added enthusiastically. 'What sort of things?'

'People, places—anything that takes my fancy.' Daniel began to manoeuvre the vehicle out of the school car park.

'And do you manage to make a living out of it?' Cathy asked. She saw Daniel frown a little and immediately regretted her question. 'Sorry!' she said quickly. 'Don't answer that. I ask all the wrong questions! It's just nice, that's all, to talk to someone who understands what it's like not to have very much money. Most of the occupants of Langforde,' she added, glancing at the impressive stonebricked country houses which lined the green, 'don't seem to be particularly troubled in that area.'

'No, you're right. This is a fairly wealthy village,' Daniel murmured. 'Lots of captains of industry seem to retire here.'

'Do you sell many of your paintings?'

'A certain amount. It fluctuates. More often than not I'm loath to part with any of them. I really should devote more time to it if I'm to make any real headway.'

'I feel that way about my bits and pieces,' Cathy murmured. 'I haven't thrown myself into it wholeheartedly as yet, but I want to at some point in the future.'

'Bits and pieces?' His attractive mouth curved. 'Sounds intriguing.'

'Oh, it's not… Well, at least…' Cathy found herself blushing under Daniel's interested gaze. 'I…I make things.'

'What kind of things?'

She didn't usually talk about her craftwork. 'Oh, things for the garden: bird boxes and plant holders, labels, signs, that kind of thing. Nothing really remarkable.'

'And you sell them?'

'When I get the chance. At the moment it really is just a few pounds every now and then.' Cathy hesitated. 'That's what upset me so much when I was talking to Miss Stubbs. She made me feel…inadequate.' Cathy looked down at the unlovely overalls she was wearing. 'Do you find people look down at you because you haven't got much money?'

'No…' Daniel's dark brows drew together in a deep frown. 'No, I can't say I do.'

Now this was one hell of a dilemma! Where had she got the idea that he had no money? He glanced around the interior of the Land Rover; it needed cleaning out, as usual, and the clothes he was wearing…they were clean but, as was often the case, not exactly the smartest garments in his wardrobe.

'I expected to feel a little out of place, of course,' Cathy continued. 'This is a picture-postcard village and obviously there are a great many people with money who live here, but even so—'

'You really mustn't let what Miss Stubbs said upset you,' Daniel asserted. 'Forget it. She doesn't know what she's talking about.' He negotiated the Land Rover around a tight bend in the road and debated whether to put Cathy straight about his situation. He glanced sideways. She looked so…earnest, so fragile. There was a vulnerability, too, beneath the smiling exterior. He decided to keep quiet, for the moment at least. Somehow it didn't seem appropriate to tell her of his wealth, the fact that he could have afforded to spend every day of the week doing unpaid work of one kind or another, whereas she… Daniel frowned and shook his head.

'What's the matter?'

'Sorry?' He turned to look at her. Dark eyes surveyed the pale skin and delicately shaped mouth, and he knew in that moment that he would do everything in his power to nurture this new relationship.

'You look preoccupied and you shook your head. I just thought something might be wrong.'

'No, everything's fine.' Daniel glanced across at her and smiled reassuringly. 'So! How is everything? The cottage coming together?'

'Yes, it's coming along just fine. As you can see I've abandoned everything to try and get it organised as quickly as possible.'

Daniel frowned slightly. 'Abandoned...?'

'Myself.' Cathy pulled a face. 'I felt such a scruff talking to Miss Stubbs. I feel a scruff now,' she admitted self-consciously. 'I rushed out of the house... I've probably got paint all over my face.'

'You look...' Daniel struggled to think of an appropriate description. How would she react if he said what he really thought? he wondered. That she looked utterly appealing with her large green eyes and tangled hair?

'There's no need to say anything,' she asserted firmly. 'I know how awful I look—like someone who's been dragged through a hedge backwards!'

'I like the tousled look.' Daniel kept his voice deliberately light. 'It suits the countryside.'

'Mummy, look at those lambs!' Robbie exclaimed excitedly. 'There are lots and lots in that field.'

'Oh, yes!' Cathy linked an arm around Robbie's shoulder and stroked the soft skin of his neck. 'Aren't they sweet?' He looked happy now, eyes intent on the road ahead, craning his neck this way and that to look at new things.

'You aren't covered in paint, by the way,' Daniel murmured. His mouth curved into a stunning smile. 'Just in case you were wondering.'

'Well, that's something.' Cathy looked into his face and their eyes met for a brief moment. Oh, he was *so* handsome. She blushed and looked away, feeling self-conscious, fearful that he might be able to read her thoughts. It wasn't difficult to imagine the sort of woman he would attract— some svelte, beautiful creature with scarcely a hair out of place. I must look like a man, she thought miserably. Damn! Why didn't I think to change before I came out to fetch Robbie this afternoon? These awful overalls...

She was being ridiculous again. What did it matter how she looked? Daniel was a kind, thoughtful person, who had happened to be in the vicinity when she needed a little support. The fact that he was stunningly handsome and had a body like Adonis wasn't in the least relevant.

'Have you lived here all your life?' Cathy asked, risking a quick glance at his muscled arms and strong profile, then keeping her gaze fixed firmly on the way ahead.

'Is it that obvious?' His smile was relaxed. 'Yes, pretty much. I spent a few years travelling, backpacking around various continents; you know, the usual student kind of thing.' Daniel glanced down at Robbie sitting between them and smiled ruefully. 'Then again, maybe you don't. I should imagine in your early twenties you were preoccupied with rather more important things.'

'Yes.' Cathy tousled Robbie's hair. 'You could say that.'

She turned her head away to look out at the passing fields. She felt tired, and ridiculously tearful suddenly. Why? Because Daniel had mentioned a situation that she could never in her wildest dreams have experienced? No, it wasn't that. Having Robbie might have altered the whole course of her life, but she didn't regret it, not for a second.

Cathy inhaled a steadying breath. She really did just feel incredibly tired, that was all. The strain of not only months, but years of having to cope on her own sometimes crept up and caught her out.

Daniel cursed inwardly. Hell! Why didn't he ever think before he spoke? He wished he hadn't mentioned travelling around the world. What an idiotic subject to bring up. He tried to calculate her age. Young, that was for sure. How old would she have been when she'd had Robbie? Eighteen, nineteen, maybe? She had such a beautiful mouth, Daniel thought, and her eyes were such an intense green, fringed with dark lashes. He found that he liked the fact that she didn't have a scrap of make-up on—that she was fresh and natural and unsure of herself.

'Robbie did some great work today, didn't you, champ!'

'I drew the flats,' Robbie announced proudly. 'I drew in Amy and Mrs Brownfield and Mr Peters. They were waving from the windows.'

Cathy smiled at her son. 'Perhaps you could send it to Amy,' she murmured. 'I'm sure she'd love to put it up on her wall.'

And he loved the sound of her voice: husky when she was tired or upset, like now. He saw the tears glistening in her eyes and worked at keeping his voice light. 'That sounds like a good idea, Robbie. We'll make sure we get it finished next week when I'm in school. You can add colour and mount it on some good strong card so it doesn't get ruined in the post.'

They had arrived at the cottage. Daniel glanced through the windscreen at the ramshackle house, with its rickety front porch and ill-fitting windows, and felt a surge of concern.

'Would you like to come in for a cup of tea? Of course, if you're busy…' Cathy added swiftly. 'If you've got something else to do—'

'Not a thing!' His mouth curved into a stunning smile. 'Thanks! I thought you'd never ask.'

Daniel, standing in the kitchen, surveyed the cheerful yellow room with obvious admiration. 'Hey, this is great!' If he hadn't witnessed the transformation with his own eyes, he would never have believed it possible. He glanced across at Cathy's paint-splattered figure. She looked stunning: fresh and full of vitality, the shine of pleasure in her eyes, a delectable curve to her mouth which couldn't be ignored. 'You are amazing!' he added with genuine feeling. 'To have accomplished so much in such a short space of time—'

'Oh, I don't know about that…' Her expression told him

that she wasn't used to compliments. 'It's a lot better than when you last saw it,' she agreed. 'But then considering the state it was in, that's probably not saying a great deal,' she added dryly.

'Don't be so modest. You've done a marvellous job.' Daniel frowned slightly, training his gaze more closely on Cathy's face. The eyes were still shining, the smile was still there, but beneath the expression of warm delight he could detect traces of ingrained fatigue. 'You must be absolutely exhausted,' he asserted.

'Just a bit. Actually, some evenings this week I've found myself falling asleep over my dinner; I must admit I've never done that before.'

Daniel's frown deepened. What could he do to help her? Offer the services of his trusty cleaner, who came in a couple of times a week? Pay for a decorator to come in and relieve her of the burden of painting every room? He released a breath. Difficult. He hardly knew her. Although something told him that even a close association wouldn't mean she would accept outside help readily.

'You're on a mission, aren't you?' Daniel asserted quietly. He held her gaze, found it was a struggle to drag his eyes away from her face. 'All this...' He glanced around the room. 'This is something you've wanted to do for a long while.'

'How did you...?' Her voice was husky. Daniel's heart twisted a little at the sound of it.

'And you're pleased—now that it's happened?' he asked.

'Oh, yes!' Cathy's mouth curved into a stunning smile. She felt more happy in this moment than she had in a long, long while. Everything suddenly fell into sharp focus: the bright, sharp yellow of the kitchen, the sunshine streaming through the uncurtained window, the sound of Robbie's young voice suddenly bursting into song. Daniel.

'You're happy.' She was. Daniel's smile held pleasure and relief. 'I'm glad.'

Her heart was thudding fit to burst. This was incredible, having him here, talking to her like this—as if he really cared...

'Oh, yes!' Cathy forced herself to turn away and began filling the kettle at the now gleaming stainless-steel sink.

Robbie rushed past, still singing, and pushed open the door which led through into the front room. 'Can I look?' Daniel asked, glancing back at Cathy.

She lifted her shoulders, eyes shining, happy that he was interested enough to bother. 'Be my guest.'

She followed him through into the room a moment later, standing apart, glancing at his face from time to time to gauge his reaction, wondering how such a gorgeous, kind man had managed to enter her life—even if it was only in the acquaintance category. For when had she *ever* discovered a man who wasn't selfish or egotistical or, as in a particular person's case, downright cruel?

'Now this is even more impressive!'

Cathy dragged her thoughts away from Steve and blushed with pleasure. 'It's all cosmetic,' she murmured, eyeing the pale cream walls and muslin drapes, which did a good job of hiding the rotten windowframes and damp patches near to the windows. 'Just cleaning and a fresh coat of paint.'

'This surely can't be that old sideboard?' Daniel ran an appreciative hand over the newly painted surface.

'Yes, it is.'

'How did you achieve this finish?' He looked across at her with obvious interest, dark eyes intense and compelling. 'It's totally changed the look of the thing.'

He was irresistible. Cathy had simply never encountered any man who was so kind and humorous and so thoroughly attractive before. Her thoughts flitted briefly into fantasy land, but she dragged them back—not without a certain amount of reluctance. It could never happen, she told herself. Don't even begin to kid yourself...

'Oh, it's just several layers of toning paint, then I rub it down with sandpaper and reveal the colour as much or as little as I want...' Cathy paused, conscious of the effect Daniel's gaze was having on her. 'Everything's done on a shoestring,' she continued hurriedly. 'Wicker's good for storage, and you can buy it quite cheaply...'

Robbie stopped singing and began to make the sound of a very throaty engine; cars skidded across the wooden floor and Cathy smiled across at Daniel. 'And it fits in with the look. These rugs too. Of course they're not wool or anything,' she added, glancing down at the rush matting, 'but the carpet that was in here was so disgusting I decided to just wash the floorboards beneath and do it this way.' Cathy inhaled a steadying breath, conscious that she was becoming perhaps a little too enthusiastic. But after working so hard all week it was lovely having someone come in and compliment her on her efforts like this. 'I could show you how to do the paint effect some time, if you like,' she offered.

'Thanks.' Daniel's smile was warm. 'I'd like that.'

'Furniture is *so* expensive, isn't it?' Cathy continued. 'I find most of my stuff in junk shops and then do it up; do you ever do that?'

'Er...no.' Daniel shook his head. 'I can't say I do.'

'Oh, you really ought to. You'd save a fortune! There's a place not far from here—'

Daniel loved watching her as she spoke. Her eyes were alight, her voice vibrant with enthusiasm. He knew there was no way he could admit to being wealthy—not now at any rate.

'The one off the Cranton road?'

'Yes, that's right!' She looked pleased that he knew it. 'Perhaps we could...?' He watched as she hesitated, saw the way her beautiful green eyes narrowed in confusion. 'Of course you're probably busy—'

'Not at all. At least...' He thought of the work for his family's charity foundation which was piled on his desk at home, then thrust it from his mind. 'I'd like to take a look at it.'

'You've got the Land Rover too,' Cathy continued. 'It would be no trouble to get pieces home, would it?'

'No, I suppose not.' Daniel smiled. 'If you ever want me to pick something up for you—'

'Oh, no!' Cathy flushed. 'I didn't mean… I wasn't trying to hint that I—'

'I know you weren't.' Daniel cut through her embarrassed response briskly. 'But the offer stands.' Dark eyes held her gaze. 'If you ever need any help, don't hesitate to ask.' He thought for a moment, and succumbed. 'How about a trip out there on Monday? It's open every day of the week, I believe. I've seen the furniture piled up outside when I've driven past.'

'Really?' Cathy paused. 'Are you sure?'

'Positive.' Her smile, Daniel decided, really was the best thing he had ever seen. 'How about we get there early to pick up all the bargains?' he suggested.

'Are you sure? Only…on Monday, if you've got something else to do…'

'Cathy, stop frowning.' Daniel's voice was light, but there was a semi-serious look in his eyes. 'I made the offer. I'm not the sort of man who says one thing and means another.'

'Oh, but the school is closed that day for repairs, isn't it? That means Robbie—'

'No problem. We'll take him too.'

'Well, in that case…' Cathy's mouth curved. 'That would be lovely—thank you.'

He should leave; he had a million things to do… Daniel smiled. 'Any chance of seeing the rest of the house?' he asked suddenly.

'…and this is my bedroom. But, as you can see, I haven't done anything to it yet—apart from clean it, of course.'

He looked around the depressing room. The wallpaper

was peeling and there were several damp patches on the walls. Daniel worked hard at keeping a neutral expression, but it wasn't easy. He hated to think of Cathy having to sleep somewhere like this. She was so fresh and lovely... 'What did you hope to do with it?' He heard the scepticism in his own voice, and wondered if Cathy heard it too.

'Oh...' He saw from her expression that she had. 'I haven't given it much thought—not yet. I've been too busy with the rest of the house. Anyway, the spare bedroom is next on my agenda.'

'The spare room?' Daniel frowned. 'What on earth for?'

'It's going to be my workroom—you know, for the bits and pieces I make?' Cathy walked across to the window and looked out. 'Isn't this a glorious view?' she said, smiling happily. 'I can hardly believe I'm standing in my own bedroom, staring at...' She paused, counting silently. 'Four horses and twenty-one—no, twenty-two sheep!'

Daniel crossed the room and stood beside her. The urge to take her in his arms was almost overwhelming. He shook his head slightly, amazed by the strength of desire she engendered in him.

'What is it?' She was looking up at him, smiling quizzically.

'Nothing...' She clearly had no idea. He looked out at the rolling green countryside with new eyes—the eyes of the woman beside him—and understood how much this must mean to her. 'You've just made me wonder whether I really appreciate all this enough.'

'I'm sure you do. I'm a bit crazy at the moment—all this...' She gestured towards the view. 'I've always wanted to live in the country,' Cathy murmured softly. 'It's been a dream for as long as I can remember.'

'And now you're here.'

She looked up at him, her eyes wide, her expression more lovely than he had ever known. 'Yes.'

Daniel smiled. 'I'm glad.'

'Really?' She seemed touchingly surprised by his response.

'Really,' he repeated gently.

'Would you like to look at the sort of thing I make?' she asked suddenly, gesturing towards the door. 'It's nothing grand, but I enjoy it and it means a bit extra for treats every now and then.' They walked into the spare room together. Cathy lifted an item out of a large box. *'Voilà!'* she announced cheerfully.

Daniel took the wooden object, twisting it around in his hands to examine it. 'This is good,' he asserted. 'For wellington boots, right?'

Cathy nodded, looking pleased. 'Right,' she agreed. 'That one isn't quite finished yet.'

'This is, though.' Daniel lifted out a bird-feeder. 'It's very good,' he commented. 'So, where do you plan to sell these? Did you know there's a country fair coming up next week?'

'Yes.' Cathy nodded. 'But I don't think I'm ready for that league. I haven't got that much stock, and anyway a fair of that size will be for the professional traders, won't it?'

'Actually, others do attend.' Daniel placed the bird-feeder back in its box. 'Individuals like yourself, who make things as a hobby.'

'Do they?' Cathy's expression brightened. 'Oh, well, perhaps next year, then,' she replied. 'I expect just about everybody in the village goes, do they?'

'Just about,' Daniel agreed. 'It's tied up with the ball.'

'Oh, yes, that sounds very grand.'

Daniel picked up another item: a neatly painted plant holder. A frown creased his forehead. 'Yes, it is rather. Actually—'

'Mummy, is it time for my programme yet?' Robbie rushed, breathless, into the room. 'I can't find the remote.'

Cathy glanced at her watch. 'Yes, sweetheart! Channel one. And it's probably down the side of the settee, as usual!

Come on, let's go and see if we can find it.' She glanced back towards Daniel with a smile. 'Sorry about this.'

'There's no need to apologise. In fact...' Daniel pulled back his cuff and glanced at his wristwatch. He had been on the verge of telling Cathy about his connection with the ball and the fair, but now the moment had passed he didn't feel like pursuing it. 'I have to go.' He exhaled a breath.

'You're late for something?' Cathy enquired. She frowned. 'I'm sorry. Here I am, wittering on—'

'You are not wittering.' Daniel smiled. 'I wish I didn't have to go, but I do.'

'Sorry. It really is my fault for keeping you. Thanks very much for the lift. It was much appreciated—so were the compliments about my efforts at decorating too, come to that!' Cathy began descending the stairs. Daniel followed behind, aware of his own reluctance now that the time had come to leave.

'Until Monday, then.' Daniel smiled. He found he wanted to kiss her—very much. But he held out his hand instead, in what felt like a ridiculously formal mode of parting. 'Thanks for the cup of tea.'

'You've been very kind.'

'Have I?' Daniel's mouth twisted into a wry smile. A ray of brilliant sunshine flooded into the hallway as Cathy opened the front door. 'Believe it or not,' he added lightly, 'but kind has very little to do with it...'

CHAPTER FOUR

When the doorbell rang at seven o'clock that same evening, Cathy felt sure it would be Daniel. She laid down the book she and Robbie had been reading together and got up quickly. 'Robbie, do I look all right?' she asked, smoothing down her hair, relieved that she had at least changed out of her tatty overalls into some old, but rather cleaner denims.

'Yes, Mummy, you look very nice.' Her son's thoughts were on the same wavelength. 'If it's Daniel, can I make him a peanut butter sandwich, do you think?'

Cathy smiled. 'We'll see. He may have just eaten his dinner.'

The question didn't arise, because it wasn't him, it was Sandra. Cathy, standing with her hand on the front door, couldn't help feeling more than a little crestfallen.

'Cathy! Hello! Sorry to drop by unannounced, but I was passing and I saw your light—'

'Hello!' Cathy forced a welcoming smile. 'Had a good week?'

'Oh, you know—busy, busy, busy!' Sandra didn't bother to ask how Cathy's had been. She stepped gingerly across the threshold. 'How *do* you put up with this?' she asked bluntly, glancing around the dismal hallway.

'Well, you know, beggars can't be choosers.' Cathy replied, trying not to allow Sandra's bluntness to get to her. 'I've seen a lot worse.'

'Have you?' It was all Sandra could do to repress a shudder. 'Where?'

'Well, the place I've just moved from wasn't exactly the Ritz!' Cathy replied cheerfully. 'Come on through; it's a lot better in here.' She waited for a reaction from Sandra as she entered the new, improved living room, but none was forthcoming. 'Robbie, say hello to Sandra.'

Robbie offered up a brief, toothy grin. 'We thought you were Daniel,' he said, sounding disappointed. 'I was going to make him a peanut butter sandwich.'

'Really?' A flicker of surprise crossed Sandra's face. She looked across at Cathy questioningly. That was the only trouble with five-year-olds, Cathy thought. They always said what they were thinking. 'Are you expecting him, then?'

'Oh, no! We met him earlier this afternoon at school, that's all. Robbie's rather taken with him.'

'Ah!' Sandra's expression cleared. 'Well, you'll have to join the queue, Robbie!'

'What queue?' He looked around, as if to try and find it. 'Like at a shop, do you mean?'

'No, not at a shop…' Sandra lifted her shoulders and looked towards Cathy for help.

'Would you like a cup of tea?' she asked.

'No, thanks. In fact, I'm in quite a rush; I've dropped by straight from work and there's masses to do at home. No. You see, the reason I'm here is to ask you whether you'd like to come to a little party I'm having.'

'Oh, a party?' Cathy repeated, as if she had hardly heard of such a thing.

'Yes! I haven't had anyone around for ages, and I thought it would be a good way for you to get to know some people in the village.'

'That's very nice of you.' Cathy smiled, mentally adjusting her opinion of Sandra a degree or two. 'But I'm not sure—'

'Oh, do come!' Sandra made it sound as if the whole evening would be ruined just because of her non-attendance. 'Couldn't you find someone to babysit?'

'I'm not a *baby*!' Robbie protested indignantly.

'It's just a figure of speech.' Robbie looked at Sandra blankly. 'A saying,' she added, with an edge of impatience.

'Don't worry about it, darling,' Cathy told him. 'Actually, yes, I do think I could find someone to look after Robbie,' she added, addressing Sandra again. It was faintly astonishing to Cathy that she might actually be able to accept the invitation. 'Mrs Barnet,' she explained. 'She lives next door. She's been very helpful all week. She's said she'd be more than happy to come round if ever I need a sitter.'

'Then you'll come?'

Cathy hesitated. 'When is it?'

'Why?' Sandra's smile was faintly condescending. 'Have you got other engagements? It's on Sunday evening, actually,' she continued. 'I know it's quite short notice,' she added, seeing the surprise on Cathy's face, 'but I'm rather impulsive, and I was sitting at my desk at work… I would have had it tomorrow evening, but I'm doing something myself.' She waved her beautifully manicured hands in a frivolous gesture. 'And I thought, why not?'

'I'll have to check with Mrs Barnet.' Cathy glanced down at Robbie, who was looking intently at his book. 'But if Robbie's happy and she doesn't mind…'

'Well, shall we say that if I *don't* hear from you, then I'll assume you're coming?' Sandra responded briskly. She glanced around the front room, which was looking its best now, mainly due to the lack of light. 'So you and Daniel have become properly aquainted, then? Of course,' she added, 'you should be realistic about this little friendship you seem to have struck up with him. It doesn't do to get carried away. Too much fantasising only leads to disappointment. I don't mean it as an insult—don't get me wrong,' she added, smiling charmingly, 'but you're not exactly…well, you know…in the same league as Daniel, are you?'

Cathy thought about her face and her figure. 'No,' she admitted, managing to keep her voice remarkably neutral.

'No, I don't suppose I am. Will he be attending your party?' she asked suddenly.

'No.' Sandra released a sigh. 'I phoned and asked him, but he said he had a prior engagement. I had been hoping he'd come, but he is a very busy man, I suppose. It's the ball next Thursday, and I had sort of planned to be very bold and ask him... But never mind,' she added briskly, her immaculately painted lips splitting into a smile. 'There'll always be another opportunity.' Sandra stood up suddenly. 'Now we've finished discussing my favourite subject,' she announced, 'I think I'd better be off.'

Cathy followed her guest out into the hallway.

'I'll hopefully see you on Sunday, then! Around eight o'clock. You do know where I live—it's the thatched cottage on the left side of the green. Not far from the shop. You can't miss it. Oh!' She turned back towards Cathy. 'My parties are usually rather smart, dressy occasions.' Her gaze drifted to the depressing hallway. 'That's all right, isn't it?'

'Umm...' Cathy hesitated, visualising the dreary contents of her wardrobe. She hadn't given a thought about what she might wear. 'Well...there is a dress which I've had for quite a while,' she murmured. 'It's purple silk. A friend gave it to me, but I'm not sure—'

'Sounds perfect,' Sandra responded smoothly. 'I do so like it when my guests have obviously made an effort.'

'You're sure everyone will dress up? Only I don't want to stand out like a sore thumb,' Cathy murmured. 'This dress is quite...striking.'

'Absolutely! Honestly, it sounds just the thing,' Sandra replied confidently. 'Do wear it; there's nothing worse than being dressed in the wrong style, is there? Well, I'll see you Sunday evening, then!' she added, smiling brightly.

High heels clicked imperiously down the garden path. Sandra slid her svelte form behind the wheel of a shiny red sports car, and with a casual wave of her hand roared off into the night.

The next forty-eight hours saw Cathy in a muddle of indecision. One minute she wanted to go to the party, the next found her looking for any excuse, just so that she could phone Sandra and tell her she wouldn't be able to make it.

The coward's way out definitely appealed. It wasn't going to be her sort of thing, she kept telling herself—not at all. A Chinese takeaway and a video was about the extent of her social experience.

On the other hand—and Cathy worked hard at putting forward the positive point of view—it would be a chance to meet a few more people from the village. She wanted to stop feeling like an interloper as quickly as possible, for Robbie's sake as much as her own, and she wouldn't get to that stage unless she made an effort to socialise with the locals, would she?

'What do you think of Mummy in this dress?'

Robbie, lying full stretch on the bed, looked up from his drawing and considered Cathy for all of five seconds. 'Pretty.'

'You don't think it's too...' Cathy searched for a word. 'Fancy?'

'No.' Robbie glanced up again and surveyed the swathe of purple silk. 'I like it. You look like a princess.'

Cathy smiled. 'Thank you, sweetheart. You say the nicest things.' She smoothed the silky fabric over her hips and considered herself in the mirror. She wasn't sure. She had inherited it from a friend years ago, and kept it purely because she loved the colour so much. The trouble was, admiring it when it was hanging on a rail was one thing; actually wearing it out was quite another.

But then what were the alternatives? Cathy flicked through the paltry number of hangers, half hoping she might come across a garment by magic. No chance. She knew every item hanging there, and all of them were either too old, too tatty, or too uninspiring to be suitable.

It was a little tight. Cathy swivelled around and inspected

the bulging zip at the side. If she wore this then she'd have to breathe in all evening, that was for sure. What about shoes? Another problem. Cathy knew exactly the sort that would look good with a dress like this: strappy, high and black. Unfortunately her only decent pair were blue suede, with a too-chunky heel. Well, they were at least smart, that was something, she supposed. They didn't look totally ridiculous, but they weren't ideal either. Still, she possessed no others, apart from the boots she wore with her jeans and trousers, so they would just have to do.

Now for the *pièce de résistance*. Cathy retrieved the matching feather boa from a box on the floor and flung it around her neck. 'Robbie!' She struck a laughing pose. 'What do you think?'

'Hey!' He jumped off the bed and grabbed at the end, nearly throttling Cathy in the process. 'What's that? It's great! Can I try it?'

He played with it for ages, whilst Cathy attempted to tame her hair into something approaching a sophisticated style. She decided on a coiled arrangement positioned low down at the nape of her neck and just hoped it would stay fixed.

'Here you are, Mummy.' Robbie carefully wound the boa around her neck.

Cathy smiled. 'Thank you, sweetheart, but I'm not going to wear it.'

'Why not?' He wrapped his arms around her neck. 'It's pretty.'

'Is it?' Cathy smiled at their joint reflection in the mirror opposite for a moment, then turned and kissed his cheek. 'Now, are you sure you don't mind me going out this evening?' she asked, half hoping Robbie would have a sudden change of heart and insist she stay at home. 'You know where I'll be?'

'At Sandra's.' He raised his eyes. 'You've told me again and again.'

'And you're sure you don't mind me going out?'

'No, I don't mind. But you've got to wear this.' Robbie wrapped the boa a couple more times around Cathy's neck. 'It's funny.'

'Cheeky!' Cathy ruffled her son's head. 'You said it looked pretty a moment ago!' He had just had his bath and he smelt all clean and fresh. 'Mmm, you're so cuddly!' she murmured, holding him close. 'Perhaps I won't go...' She had a sudden compulsion to take off all her finery and snuggle up with her son.

'I think you should.' He looked and sounded touchingly serious. 'You're all dressed up, and parties are great fun. Will there be jelly and those cakes with the bits on?'

'No...' Cathy thought of the sophisticated Sandra. 'Not at this party...' She released a sigh, turning back to look at her reflection in the mirror once again. She had tried to cultivate a glamorous look, but somehow lip gloss and eyeliner didn't seem to sit very comfortably on her face. 'Well, if you think I should go...'

The doorbell rang at that moment. 'That will be Mrs Barnet,' she announced brightly, forcing herself to sound positive. She gave her reflection one last glance and told herself that she didn't look that bad, just...different.

'Will she let me stay up late?' Robbie asked hopefully.

'You can go to bed at eight o'clock as it's Sunday night and there's no school tomorrow, but no later,' Cathy warned, beginning to unwind the boa from her neck. She glanced in the mirror. Oh, what the hell! she thought. It did sort of finish off the ensemble—it certainly didn't make the outfit any worse, that was for sure, and Sandra *had* said she liked her guests to make an effort. 'Come on, darling!' She held out her hands and Robbie jumped into her arms. 'Let's go and say hello to Mrs Barnet...'

It took courage just walking through the gate. Several cars were parked outside Sandra's cottage. Cathy adjusted her dress under the glare of the porch light and bit her lip against the pain of a blister. She remembered now why she hardly ever wore these shoes—her feet were killing her.

There was a light on in every window of the thatched cottage. Cathy caught sight of faces she didn't know; a middle-aged man with glasses and a floppy fringe was standing in one of the downstairs rooms with a drink in his hand. He looked a little bored. Cathy cast a quick glance over his choice of clothes—a diamond-patterned golf sweater and casual slacks—and decided he was probably feeling a little under-dressed for the occasion.

Sandra came into view. She looked as stunning as ever, with her long blonde hair brushed becomingly over her shoulders, but… Cathy frowned. Where was the little black and red lace number? No, surely not! Her heart sank. She wasn't wearing anything approaching a party dress. Cathy glanced down at the purple silk peeping beneath the edges of her coat, then looked back at the elegant trousers and plain jumper which Sandra wore.

Another couple of guests, both men, moved into view, then someone else—a woman. All of them were dressed in casual attire. *Every single one!* Cathy glanced down at her own dress in horror. Oh, no! She couldn't go in wearing this diabolical creation. She'd look a complete and utter fool!

Voices behind her. She spun round and saw a man and a woman walking up the path. Cathy glanced at their sober clothing and cringed.

'Hello! Were you just about to go in?' The man smiled and reached forward to ring the bell before Cathy could move. 'Quite chilly out here, isn't it?' The couple stood shoulder to shoulder, effectively blocking her retreat. 'Are you a friend of Sandra's?'

'Er…yes. Well…at least…that is…' Cathy stumbled over her reply. All she could think about was the awfulness of her purple dress. The couple introduced themselves, but she was hardly aware of their names. Cathy smiled briefly, wondering if there was any possible way she could keep her coat on all evening.

Sandra opened the door and the understated elegance of her outfit came into full view. 'Ah, more guests! Quite a crowd on my doorstep! Lovely to see you all!' Her gaze flicked to Cathy's figure and then away again. 'Come in, everyone! Come in!'

Cathy stumbled across the threshold and followed Sandra into a tastefully decorated sitting room. She glanced about her miserably; it was already crowded with guests.

'Let me take your coats.'

'I...I think perhaps I'll keep mine on.'

'What on earth for?' Sandra's brow creased into a frown. 'You'll roast!'

'My dress...!'

'What about your dress?' Sandra smiled gaily, and held out an expectant hand towards Cathy's coat.

'You said...you were having a party,' Cathy murmured.

'And so I am!' Sandra looked around at the gathering with a too bright smile. 'Come along, don't be shy. Give me your coat and then I'll introduce you to everyone.'

This was it, then, Cathy told herself, her moment of humiliation. She opened up her duffle coat and revealed the incongruous mix of purple silk and feathers against the rough black wool. She glanced around, aware of the sick feeling in her stomach as the other guests eyed her with interest.

'Oh, goodness!' Sandra's eyes were wide with surprised delight. 'I see what you mean.' A smile twitched the corners of her immaculately painted mouth. 'It is rather...striking, isn't it?'

I'm just going to have to brazen it out, make a joke of it, Cathy decided swiftly. What else can I do? 'Yes, isn't it fun?' she replied, hoping with all her heart that she could carry it off. 'It was either this or jeans, and I wear those each and every day, so I thought...' Her voice began to crack. She couldn't go through with it. They were all, every last one of them, dressed so casually and so elegantly. 'I thought...' she repeated miserably.

'That you'd show everyone here what an incredibly beautiful woman you are?'

Cathy didn't know whether to laugh or cry at the sound of the deep, familiar voice. Daniel! She spun around and found herself staring into wonderfully warm brown eyes. He smiled, and she saw with relief that there was no sign of mockery in his gaze. 'I'm sure we all feel incredibly dull and boring in comparison—I know I do.'

You don't look dull or boring, Cathy thought. You look...perfect. He was dressed in casual dark trousers and a crisp, open-necked white shirt. She released a tense breath, not sure whether to feel pleased or disappointed that he should see her here, looking like this. 'Hello, Daniel,' she murmured. 'I...I didn't expect to see you here.'

'Change of plan.' Dark, sensuous eyes scanned her body. His mouth curved into a humorous smile. 'Well, you certainly know how to make an entrance!'

Cathy knew what he was trying to do, and was grateful. She forced herself to reply in the same, upbeat vein. 'Oh, I try my best!'

'Well, now we've all admired Cathy's tastefully chosen outfit—' Sandra's voice dripped with sarcasm '—let me get everyone a drink.'

Cathy wished she had never come. She wished she had never trusted Sandra—and more than anything she wished Daniel hadn't been here to witness her humiliation. He knew that she looked a fool—they all did, every single guest. She had felt their eyes upon her, amused, assessing, judging. She felt awful, so exposed and embarrassed. Cathy looked across and met Sandra's cool gaze with an expression of hurt and angry disbelief. How could she have done something like this?

'Try not to feel too...' Daniel's dark head shook. He handed Cathy a glass of white wine.

'Foolish?' She raised the glass and consumed the contents in one gulp. She found she wanted to cry—very much. But she held back the tears, determined not to make more of an exhibition of herself. Surely Sandra hadn't intentionally misled her? It was so…childish, so *mean*. And why? Cathy replayed their conversation of Friday evening. Was she jealous of the attention Daniel had given her? Had it been an opportunity too good to miss—was that it? I'm so naive, Cathy thought. What on earth made me think that she was my friend?

'Feel any better now?'

'Not really, no.' Cathy swept a hand across her hot forehead. 'But thanks for asking anyway.' She paused. 'It's probably almost as embarrassing for you, having to stand here and talk to me.'

'Don't say that.' Dark brows drew together in a frown. 'I don't give a damn about what other people think—sorry!' He shook his head slightly. 'That sounded bad.' His gaze was steady on her face. He looks different, Cathy told herself. What is it? More…put together, more refined. The rugged edges were still there, but there was an air of easy sophistication that she had never noticed before. 'I *want* to talk to you,' Daniel continued. His mouth curved in a stunning smile and Cathy felt the familiar twist of awareness, deep in the pit of her stomach. 'I'm glad you're here.'

Cathy shook her head. 'You're very kind,' she murmured. She attempted a smile. 'You must be heartily fed up with rescuing me by now.'

'Not at all.'

Cathy glanced down at herself. 'I should have worn my old jeans—anything would have been preferable to this abominable creation. It's awful, isn't it?'

'Pretty terrible, yes.' Daniel's expression was light. 'I do like your feather boa, though,' he murmured, a twist of a smile curving his mouth. He reached forward and lifted the end. 'Very art deco!'

She knew what he was doing, of course, but she just wasn't in the mood to be humoured—not even by Daniel. 'No, you don't!' she replied somewhat wearily. 'Robbie did, though; he's half the reason I'm wearing it. Listen to me!' She placed a hand to her hot forehead. 'Blaming my own son now for dressing like a complete and utter fool.'

'Didn't Sandra mention the type of evening it was when she invited you?'

'Yes...she said...' Cathy exhaled a breath. 'Oh, it doesn't matter.' She shook her head and felt pins fall from her hair. 'It's done now.' She raised a hand and surreptitiously tried to thrust them back in. 'Anyway, it's my own fault for not having a mind of my own.'

Daniel was looking at her hair. 'Would you like some help?'

'No.' Cathy's voice was sharp. 'Sorry!' She handed her empty glass to Daniel and scooped her tresses up with both hands. 'I don't mean to be edgy.'

'Do you want to leave?'

'Yes, but I'm not going to.' Cathy was adamant suddenly. 'I wouldn't want to give Sandra the satisfaction!'

'What did she say to you?' Daniel's dark eyes narrowed. He looked fierce suddenly. 'I thought you two were friends.'

'So did I. At least, I thought there was the possibility of becoming friends.' Cathy replied, glancing across the room to where Sandra was standing. 'She led me to believe that tonight was a party—a real dressy, fun kind of evening. I mentioned this dress and she said it sounded fine. Of course, there's always the possibility that she changed her mind and forgot to let me know...'

'You don't believe that for a minute.'

Cathy met Daniel's steady gaze. 'No, I don't suppose I do.' She saw that Sandra was making her way over. 'I think I'll go and get myself another drink and maybe mingle a bit.' She forced a bright smile. 'I've coped with the worst of the humiliation, haven't I? Apart from the fact that nobody here will ever be able to look me in the eye again without remembering this damned dress—what else could possibly happen?'

'You really shouldn't worry about what people think—'

'Easy for you to say!' Cathy replied swiftly. 'Do you *know* how handsome you look?'

Daniel's mouth curved into a gorgeous smile. 'A compliment?'

'Of course!' Cathy cast bleak eyes over Daniel's impressive frame and told herself this was how it had to be—the only way it *could* be. After all, hadn't she always prided herself on her realism? Sandra might be a manipulative nymphomaniac, but she was right about one thing: Cathy didn't stand a chance with someone as gorgeous as Daniel. 'And there was I imagining poor, struggling artists very rarely wore anything except a paint-spattered smock and a floppy beret!' she added lightly.

'Actually, Cathy...' Daniel's dark brows drew together in a frown. 'There's something I've been meaning to talk to you—'

'Daniel!' Sandra's silky tones interrupted whatever he had been about to say. 'How nice of you to keep Cathy company!'

'If you'll excuse me, I'm feeling a little cold.' Cathy avoided Sandra's amused gaze. She didn't think she could bear a three-way conversation with Sandra looking so annoyingly smug and sophisticated. 'I think I'll go and stand by the fire to get warm.'

'Yes, you do that, Cathy,' Sandra's voice was rich with amusement. 'Now, Daniel...'

Cathy didn't hear any more She crossed the low-ceilinged room, picking up another glass of wine from a side table on the way, conscious of how much more comfortable and stylish this cottage was in comparison to her own barren accommodation. She raised the glass to her lips, drinking the red wine swiftly, only wondering when it was too late whether she shouldn't be a little more cautious, given the fact that she hadn't eaten a thing all evening. She felt woozy—less embarrassed, though; that was something. Now I know why people turn to drink, she thought. It certainly dulled the senses…

She stared down at the flames in miserable contemplation, thinking about Robbie and Daniel and the mess she had managed to make of the evening simply because she didn't have a clue about clothes and good taste…

'Cathy!' There was a sudden shout. She lifted her head to look across the room and saw Daniel rushing towards her.

'What?' She frowned. Her heart was pounding in her chest. 'What is it?'

'Cathy, for heaven's sake—!' He grabbed hold of her arm and pulled her away from the fireplace. 'You're on fire!'

It wasn't a joke.

Cathy dragged her gaze away from Daniel's concerned expression. She became aware of an acrid burning smell, glanced down, twisted sharply, and gave an exclamation of horror as it became apparent that the feather boa was alight.

'Quickly!' Daniel's hands flew to her neck. He unwound the treacherous item and threw the flaming feathers onto the hearth. Cathy stood shaking, watching in horror as he scuffed out the flames. A pungent smell filled the room.

'Heavens! What on earth—?' Sandra approached, followed by most of the other guests, all of them clearly unable to believe their eyes.

'Just a slight accident,' Daniel murmured. 'There's nothing to worry about.'

'Goodness, the smell!' Sandra exclaimed, in her best stage voice. She put her hand to her nose and pulled a face. 'It's disgusting.'

'You can open a window.' Daniel's reply was edged with steel. 'It's not the end of the world.'

It is to me, Cathy thought. She closed her eyes for a

moment to prevent the fall of tears. 'I'm sorry,' she mumbled. 'So sorry…' She wanted to hang on, to brazen it out, but she couldn't do it. Cathy heard Daniel murmur something soothing, but it only served to make her feel worse. 'Excuse me!' She shook her head and sniffed. 'I think…excuse me!' she repeated, somewhat desperately, blindly pushing through the throng towards the front door.

It was cold outside. Cathy moved away from the lighted porch and flew up the garden path with tears streaming down her face. What a disaster! She felt such a *fool*! What on earth had she been thinking of? To imagine that this dress— She stared down at herself in disgust, releasing a growl of frustration.

The front door opened. She glanced back as a stream of light spilled into the darkness. Daniel appeared. He strode down the path with her coat in his hand. 'It's cold; you'll need this.' He held it out to her, dark eyes fixed on her face.

'Not trying to persuade me to stay, then?' Cathy queried bitterly. She wasn't sure if she wanted to see Daniel right now—not after such humiliation. For, if she were honest, it wasn't the opinion of the others which mattered so much to her but his. Only his. She wiped a hand over her eyes and allowed him to drape the duffel coat over her shoulders. 'Thanks,' she muttered.

'You're going home?'

'You don't think I'd stay after that debacle, do you?' Her tone was spiky. 'Sorry!' Cathy's shoulders drooped. 'I don't mean to take it out on you. If you hadn't removed that damned boa when you did—'

Daniel draped a comforting arm around her shoulders. 'Let me drive you.'

It felt so wonderful being this close to him. Cathy had to use all of her will-power to prevent herself sinking against his strong, rugged body, laying her weary head against his chest. She kept her body rigid. 'Are you sure? What about Sandra's little soirée?'

'She'll understand.'

'No, she won't.' Cathy glanced up into Daniel's face and saw the twist of a smile. 'She'll hate me for taking you away.'

'You're not taking me away, I'm choosing to leave—but you're right.' Dark eyes sparkled mischievously. 'Sandra won't be pleased.

'That's better,' Daniel commented approvingly, as a smile softened Cathy's expression. 'You know you'll laugh about it in the morning.'

'Will I?' She heaved a sigh. 'Maybe I will. Robbie will probably find it exciting at any rate.'

Daniel leaned forward and opened the gate. Sandra appeared, illuminated in the doorway of the cottage. 'Where are you going?' she asked imperiously.

Daniel scarcely looked back. 'I'm taking Cathy home.'

'But—!'

'Goodnight, Sandra.' Daniel's tone was cool. 'Thanks for the invitation.'

Cathy gazed about her when they were at the edge of the green. 'Where have you parked your Land Rover?'

'Actually...' Daniel was standing beside a very expensive sports car. 'I walked. Er...Colin, one of the chaps at the party, offered me his car to take you home in.'

Cathy glanced admiringly at the stylish vehicle. 'That's very nice of him. Goodness,' she added, a moment later, as Daniel unlocked the doors and she slipped into the leather passenger seat. 'This is amazing!' She leant her head against the headrest and closed her eyes, then sat bolt upright. 'What about my dress? Do you think I'll mark the seat?'

'Don't worry about it. The owner of this car is a very relaxed guy. He won't mind.'

Daniel glanced across. He felt so sorry for her. She couldn't have got it more wrong if she had tried. Her dress was suitable for a Christmas party, perhaps, something a little more lively, but not here, not for Sandra's casually tasteful soirée. He wanted to protect her. She looked *so* miserable, so lost, so…incongruous. Daniel inhaled a steadying breath. More than anything he found that he wanted to take her in his arms, to hold her close, to kiss that sweet, vulnerable mouth…

Cathy frowned. 'Are you sure? Maybe if I sit on my coat—'

'Forget it, Cathy. Stop worrying.'

'OK.' She released a sigh and sat back. 'Can you imagine how marvellous it must be,' she murmured wearily, 'to be able to *afford* something as expensive as this?'

'You'd like to be wealthy?' Daniel's large, masculine frame filled the interior. He turned the key in the ignition and the car purred into life.

'Wouldn't everyone?' she murmured. 'Life would certainly be a whole lot easier.'

OK, so he should tell her. Now was the perfect opportunity, wasn't it? Daniel manoeuvred his car away from the grass verge outside Sandra's cottage and headed towards Cathy's home. She had actually brought up the subject of money—how much more of an opportunity did he need? He shook his head, annoyed with himself, not sure of his own motives for ducking the issue. Cathy would find out sooner or later about who he was, and it would be a million times better coming from him than anyone else. She might know already of course, be playing some kind of clever game…

Daniel glanced sideways and contemplated Cathy's weary expression for a second or two. He didn't think that was the case. She was the kind of woman who wore her heart on her sleeve—if she knew about his family circumstances, about how wealthy he really was, he felt sure she would have said something by now.

So, when was he going to tell her? Daniel leant back into his seat and tried to relax. Not yet, he decided. Not tonight.

*   *   *

'Cathy…sweetheart…' Daniel crouched down beside the open passenger door. 'Cathy, you're home,' he murmured softly.

'Mmm?' She turned her head and looked at him with bleary eyes.

'We're outside your cottage. Do you think you can make it into the house, or do you want me to carry you in?'

Cathy rubbed at her eyes like a child. 'I'm not drunk,' she muttered irritably, 'just tired.' She swung her legs out of the car and stood up. 'Oh, dear!' She swayed noticeably, and in a moment Daniel's strong arms were around her waist. Cathy raised a hand to her head. 'Perhaps I have had a little more to drink than I'm used to,' she murmured.

'It's the fresh air.' Daniel swung the car door shut. It felt good holding her this close. She smelt wonderful and her hair was soft against his face. He inhaled a steadying breath, conscious of the responsibility of the moment. 'Come on, let's get you into the house. Who's looking after Robbie?'

'Mmm?' Cathy heard him say something, but she didn't seem quite able to answer. She rested her head against his shoulder and closed her eyes, revelling in the feel of Daniel's arm around her waist. It felt so good to be this close, so very good; his body was warm and strong, and the feeling of masculine protection emanating from his body was like nothing she had ever experienced before. She stumbled as they negotiated the garden path, and in a moment he had swept her into his arms…

Daniel tapped on the front door and it was opened in a moment. He smiled at Mrs Barnet's gaping expression, whispered some inane comment about it being a long night, and carried Cathy across the threshold.

'Is Robbie asleep?' Daniel laid a now sleeping Cathy, gently down onto the sofa in the front room.

'Oh, yes. Went out like a light some two or three hours ago, sir.'

Daniel smiled down into the old woman's face. He

wished she hadn't called him that, was thankful that Cathy wasn't awake to hear it. 'Mrs Barnet, do you think you could do me the most enormous favour?'

'I'll try.'

'I'd be very grateful if you didn't…' He hesitated. 'What I'm trying to say is, if you happen to get into conversation with Cathy about me—'

'She hasn't a clue who you are, has she, sir?'

'Please…' Daniel placed a hand briefly on the old woman's arm. 'There really is no need to keep calling me sir. I don't deserve such deference.'

'Now don't go trying to impose your liberal views on me, young man! It's the way I've been brought up, respectful like. Can't change a habit of a lifetime, can I? My mother and my grandmother both did stints at Langforde Hall. I'm right, though, aren't I?' she whispered, glancing down at Cathy's sleeping figure. 'She mentioned you in passing the other day, and I thought to myself then, Ay up, she's not quite got the full picture.'

'And you didn't give it to her?' Daniel enquired, his dark eyes narrowed with interest.

'No, no! Not for me to do, is it? I thought to myself, Well, young Mr Hamilton will have his reasons, and who am I to go interfering?'

'That's very good of you.'

'The thing is, she's such a lovely girl, isn't she?' Mrs Barnet continued. 'She's as poor as a church mouse, poor thing!' The elderly woman threw Daniel a telling glance. 'She feels comfortable because she thinks you haven't got two pennies to rub together either. I said to her the other day, You and me, girl, are probably the only ones in the whole of this darned village who's not on an income of at least fifty thousand a year—excepting Jack Fleming, of course, in Beard's Cottage, and Ida Wikinson who lives on the other side of Marsden Lane. And she mentioned your name then, said she didn't think you were particularly well off.' Mrs Barnet touched a thoughtful Daniel on the arm. 'She feels it keenly, you know—her poverty.'

'Yes…I realise that.'

'Well, I must be getting along.'

It took Daniel a moment to hear her. He picked up the old woman's worn tweed overcoat, which was draped over the back of the settee, and helped her into it. 'Here. Thanks for this evening.' He put his hand into his trouser pocket and produced a quantity of money. 'Please?' he persisted, noting the elderly woman's hesitant expression. 'I'm sure Cathy would want you to have something for your trouble.' He pressed the notes firmly into the wrinkled hand and smiled. 'Now, let me see you to your door.'

When he returned, Cathy was still sound asleep. Daniel crouched down beside her, thinking about all the things the old woman had said. There was no doubt that this whole situation had an ironic twist to it, he mused. In the usual course of events he had to be wary about women wanting him *for* his money, not because he didn't have any.

He looked at Cathy's sleeping face, at her riot of glossy hair, spilling over her eyes, caressing her bare shoulders, and felt a surge of desire deep in the pit of his stomach.

He wanted her. He couldn't deny it any longer. She attracted him like no other woman he had ever known before. Not just physically, but in every way there was.

Daniel released a slow breath. So, how was he going to handle things from this moment onward?

CHAPTER FIVE

'DANIEL? Is that you?' Cathy propped herself up on one elbow and looked across blearily. The room was half in darkness; only the small lamp by the television was on.

'Yes, it's me.' Daniel was sitting opposite in the only other comfortable chair.

'Did I...fall asleep?'

'Yes, you did.' He heard his own voice in the silence, husky, a little hesitant. No wonder, Daniel thought, looking across to where Cathy lay; she would look this way after making love: sexily dishevelled. His dark eyes narrowed. She was sitting up now; the thin fabric of the purple dress was taut against her breasts, one shoulder was partially bare, revealing pale, delicate skin...

He had been sketching her in repose; now he longed to catch this new look on paper... Daniel surreptitiously slipped the paper and pencil he had been using into his pocket. He promised himself that there would be another opportunity to draw her in the not too distant future.

'What time is it?' Cathy combed pale fingers through her hair. Daniel watched as the few remaining pins fell silently to the floor. 'Is Mrs Barnet still here?' she asked.

'Almost eleven, and, no, she went home a couple of hours ago.'

'Oh, goodness! I didn't realise...I thought I'd only been asleep for a few minutes. You should have woken me,' Cathy responded unsteadily. 'Is Robbie—?'

'He's fine. I went to check on him a little while ago and he was fast asleep.'

She was quiet for a moment. 'What about the car?

Shouldn't you return it to…?' She frowned faintly. 'Who was it?'

Daniel hesitated. Which name had he said? He couldn't remember. 'Don't worry, it will keep.'

'But they'll want it, won't they? They'll be worried. It's very expensive, and—'

'Cathy, don't concern yourself.' Daniel's smile was warm; he spoke softly. 'It's my problem.'

His shoulders looked incredibly broad. Cathy glanced at the crisp white shirt, the opening at its neck where a tantalising amount of tanned throat could be glimpsed. She rubbed at her eyes like a little girl, and then realised belatedly that she had put make-up on. 'I must look terrible,' she murmured.

'Not from where I'm sitting.'

'You're being very kind.'

'You keep saying that.' Smouldering dark eyes held her face. Cathy found it difficult to look away. It felt as if she were in a dream. She swallowed. Her mouth felt dry—from the wine, presumably—but she wasn't drunk. Definitely not. This was real, actually happening. Daniel was still here. He could have left if he'd wanted to, but he hadn't.

'Yes… I know… I…' She shook her head, lost for words.

'You haven't known much kindness in your life, have you?' Daniel asserted quietly.

Cathy blushed and dropped her gaze, surprised by his statement, anxious not to witness the pity, or sympathy, or whatever it was in his eyes. 'Daniel, please…' Cathy stumbled to her feet, avoiding Daniel's gaze. 'I need to get out of this awful dress. God knows what I must look like!'

He rose from the chair, towering above her. Cathy gulped uneven breaths. She had never felt so aware of someone as she did right at this moment. 'You're very beautiful, Cathy. Do you know that?'

'Don't!' A frown creased her forehead. 'Please don't… I appreciate what you're trying to do, Daniel, I really do.

After the disastrous evening…' Her smile was thin. 'It's very kind of you.'

'"Kind" has nothing to do with it! What do you see when you look in a mirror?' he asked quietly.

'Nothing!'

She spun away from him, but Daniel caught her arm and tugged her in close. 'Cathy? It's a simple question.'

'Why do you need to know?' She sounded angry. 'Look, I'm just a frazzled fat girl, who hasn't done very much with her life. There!' She glared up at him. 'Satisfied?'

'Cathy, sweetheart—!'

'Look, I really don't want to have this discussion!' She shook her head. She couldn't bear for Daniel to have to sit there and spout a hundred lies in order to make her feel better. She inhaled a breath and took the easy way out. 'If you don't mind…I'm very tired.' She pretended a yawn, conscious that she had never felt more alive, more aware of another human being in the whole of her life before. She was good at this. Putting up the barriers, acting one way, feeling another. The hard shell might be difficult, but it had its uses.

'You want me to go?' Daniel waited for a response, a protest that would contradict the message in her eyes. The silence seemed to last for ever. He had never been this cautious before. Any other woman and he would have made it perfectly clear where he hoped things might lead—any other woman, he told himself, but not this one…

'I think it would be best.' Her reply was little more than a whisper. Daniel watched as she inhaled a steadying breath. 'Yes,' she repeated, in stronger tones. 'Please go.'

It was enough. He had to do the right thing. A picture of the alternative flashed into his mind. Would it really be that wrong to stay? He was more tempted than he had ever been in his life before: to feel the warmth and softness of her skin against his own, to hold and caress her body… He cursed his own vivid imagination. Persuading her would be so pleasurable… Daniel hesitated. She was looking up at him: vulnerable, unsure, a little afraid—he could see it all in her beautiful green eyes. To take advantage of all that, here, now…to have to suffer her misgivings in the morning—for there would be misgivings. He wasn't fool enough to believe in the romance of fairy stories; she would question his motives, turn whatever they had shared into something connected with sympathy or kindness or some other foolishness.

'I'll say goodnight, then.' His voice was hard with the effort of doing the right thing. He glanced down and saw the effect it had on Cathy—she seemed to shrink into herself, to grow smaller, even more vulnerable. Daniel's jaw tightened. Damn! Why did he always have to push? 'I'm sorry about this evening,' he added gently. 'I didn't mean to make things difficult.' He watched as the shield went up, as a distance crept into her eyes.

'That's all right.' She sounded cool, her features rearranged into a mask that contained little of the woman he had seen a moment ago. He watched her wordlessly for a moment, a thousand thoughts running through his mind. If he kissed her now…?

He gave himself no time to think and leant forward, watching her watching him. Slowly, oh, so slowly. No willpower. Not with this woman at any rate. Just a kiss, Daniel told himself. Just one…

His mouth was gentle, hesitant, savouring the moment. A whisper of a kiss against lips that were soft and warm. Daniel lifted a hand, slow, sure fingers stroking the smoothness of pale skin. He wanted her. The force of it came as a complete and utter shock. He increased the pressure of his mouth just a little, parting her lips with his own, aware of the desire which was surging through his body like a tidal wave. He wanted to touch her, to rip the purple dress from her body so that he could feel the warmth of her beneath his hands…

This was enough—too much maybe—a temptation that he had no right to pursue. He paused, his mouth a breath

away from her mouth, more aware than he had ever been
in his life before of the need for composure. He could feel
the tension in her body. He had expected some response,
but she hadn't moved, was still in the same position, caught
like a frightened rabbit beneath dazzling headlights. He felt
the tremble of her lips beneath his mouth, was conscious
of the rigidity of her body so close to his own and drew
back. She didn't want it, didn't want him. Here, then, he
thought, as he looked into her face set into an expression
which told him nothing of how she felt, was a new experience. Daniel cursed—himself, his approach, his impatience—disgusted with his vanity, his own inflated ego. She
doesn't want you! he mocked. Is that so difficult to believe?

Cathy hadn't known how to respond—no, that wasn't
true, she had, but she had been scared—was *still* scared,
frightened of the consequences. If they made love, if she
allowed him to get that close to her... She glanced into
Daniel's face and told herself she had been a fool to even
believe for one second that he might genuinely want her.
Why had he even bothered? She knew what she looked
like: haggard and fat and, after this evening's debacle, totally ridiculous. Sympathy? Was that what it had been? He
was kind, and she loved him for it— Not loved. Cathy's
expression grew hard. Not that word. Respected, *liked*...

Surely he didn't feel that bad about... Her feelings became more masked as she forced herself to come to terms
with the truth. Yes, yes, it was. Oh, no! *Disgust?*

'Daniel, I'm sorry—!' She saw the look—*was* that disgust in his expression?—and her heart sank and turned
cold. 'I know I'm not... What I mean is—' She struggled
to make things all right between them. The thought that
this kiss might mean the end of his friendship, even if that
friendship was based on kindness and sympathy, maybe
even pity, frightened her beyond all measure. She didn't
want to lose him; she didn't want him to think that his
rejection of her would mean she couldn't face seeing him
again.

'You don't have to say anything. This is my fault.' His voice was firm, rugged with feeling. 'I'm responsible for starting something that—'

'I still want us to be friends!' Cathy replied swiftly. She thought about the inadequacy of such an arrangement. *Friends?* Could she cope with just that? 'It's possible, isn't it?' She looked at him and there were tears in her eyes.

'Friends.' Daniel repeated the word, as if considering it for the first time. He looked faintly perplexed. 'If that's what you want…' His smile was strained. 'I don't see why not.'

'Robbie likes you very much.'

'And you?'

'And me.' Cathy struggled to keep her voice neutral. 'I like you too.'

'I've upset you. I'm sorry.' His eyes were dark and unfathomable. 'You'll be OK?'

Cathy nodded. 'Yes,' she whispered. 'Don't worry about me.'

'Easier said than done.' He wasn't smiling. In fact, she thought, he looked positively grave. He held out his hand and after a moment's hesitation she took it, her heart banging against her ribcage as she felt Daniel's firm grasp. 'I'd still like to call by tomorrow. We arranged to visit that second-hand store, remember?'

'Oh…yes!' Cathy couldn't contain her surprise and pleasure. 'Daniel…' She frowned. 'About what happened just now—'

'Forget it.' His expression was serious, almost stony. 'I made a mistake,' he added, looking down into her face. 'I'm sorry, Cathy, I really didn't mean to…' He shook his head and the look of regret was obvious to see. 'It's been a curious evening, hasn't it?' He released her hand and managed a smile. 'I'll see you later.'

The front door closed a moment later. Cathy didn't move. She wanted to cry, but the tears wouldn't come. She should be feeling relieved, she told herself. Hadn't she just escaped a monumental amount of humiliation? If Daniel had stayed... Cathy shook her head, thrusting images of how it might have been from her mind. She needed more than kindness—it was no good pretending that she would ever be the sort of woman who could enter into a relationship without commitment and passion and respect, and a whole host of other complicated and not so complicated feelings.

But *friends*? Was it possible? Would she be able to cope with the continued agony of having Daniel so near and yet so very, very far? Cathy wanted to feel relief, a sense of having done the right thing, but it wasn't easy.

All she felt was empty and alone.

'Mum! Mum! Wake up! Daniel's here!'

'What?' Cathy sat bolt upright in bed. 'Robbie, stop yelling.' She rubbed a hand across her eyes. 'What did you say?'

'Daniel's downstairs.' Robbie threw himself onto the bed. 'I looked through the window first, before I let him in.'

'What's the time?' Cathy reached for her watch and saw to her dismay that it was past nine o'clock. 'Oh, crikey!'

'Shall I make him a cup of tea while you have a bath?' Robbie suggested helpfully.

'Oh, darling, that's so sweet of you!' Cathy gave him a swift hug. 'But you know you're not to touch the boiling kettle. Tell Daniel that I'll be down in a minute and *help* him to make some tea—OK?'

'OK!' Robbie bounded out of the room enthusiastically. 'Daniel!' He was yelling again. 'Mummy says...!'

Cathy jumped out of bed as soon as Robbie had left the room. She heard the deep murmur of Daniel's voice below, grabbed a towel and skipped along to the bathroom.

It was going to have to be the natural look once again, she thought five minutes later, as she pulled on clean denims and a cream pullover. Which probably wasn't such a bad idea, she decided, glancing at herself in the bedroom mirror, not after the way she had looked last night.

'Sorry!' Cathy entered the kitchen without giving herself time to think. Besides, dwelling on what had taken place the night before wasn't going to help one little bit; she knew that. 'I overslept.'

He looked wonderful, sitting at the kitchen table with Robbie beside him, holding a mug of tea in his strong, masculine hands. He was back to his usual style, wearing denims and a rugged pullover in a dark grey marl.

Cathy experienced the by now familiar jolt she always felt whenever she laid eyes on him, and busied herself with reboiling the kettle. 'Has Robbie been looking after you?'

'Absolutely. Between the two of us we make a pretty good cup of tea. Sorry about waking you,' Daniel added. 'Maybe I'm being a little too enthusiastic.'

'Oh, no.' Cathy shook her head. Her hair was still damp. She pushed the fiery mane behind her shoulders with one hand and lifted the teapot with the other. 'I'm glad you did. All the best bargains will be gone otherwise. What sort of things are you looking for?'

Daniel hesitated. 'I think I'll just keep an open mind,' he replied casually. 'What about you?'

'Well…' Cathy pictured the contents of her purse and wished she had the courage to come clean and tell Daniel that she couldn't afford anything. 'Robbie could do with a desk of some sort, and a chair for his room, but I don't want to crowd the Land Rover with my purchases; it's you we need to get sorted out.' She sat down at the table with her tea, all too aware of Daniel's freshly washed hair and rugged, unshaven jaw, which increased his look of raw sexuality. 'Talking of vehicles, did you return that car OK?'

'Yes.' Daniel nodded briefly. 'Yes, it's fine.'

'Your friend wasn't cross? Only it must have been late by the time you got it back to him. Daniel borrowed the most amazing car to bring me home from Sandra's last night, Robbie,' Cathy explained to her son. She narrowed her brow in query, belatedly aware that he might not want to be reminded of the debacle of the previous evening. 'What sort was it?'

'A Jaguar.' Daniel's tone was flat. Cathy sipped at her tea and wished she had left well alone, for he seemed reluctant to talk about it.

'Cor! Did you make it go fast? Was it leather inside? What colour was it?' Robbie rattled off his questions at a pace. 'I've got some cars,' he added, slipping from the table. 'They're in here...' He rushed enthusiastically towards the living room.

'Sorry.' Cathy knew her face was warm. 'He's very keen.'

'It's fine.' Daniel glanced towards the front room, where Robbie was rooting around amongst his toys. 'He's a great kid. A credit to you.'

'Thank you for saying that.' Cathy released a breath. 'After what Miss Stubbs said on Friday—'

'You mustn't take any notice of her. She's been in the job too long.'

'Did she teach you?' Cathy asked, interested suddenly.

'No, I...had someone else.' He paused. 'I want us to spend the day together. Have you other plans? I thought a walk afterwards, then lunch at a pub.' Robbie yelped with pleasure. 'Someone's in favour,' he commented, with a dry smile.

'The walk sounds great, but the pub...' Cathy bit down on her lip, unhappy to have to broach the subject. 'The thing is I...I haven't got much money.' She knew she sounded awkward, but she was determined to be honest from the start. 'I'm always a bit broke at the beginning of the week—'

'Cathy, when I suggested the pub, I had no intention of letting you pay.' Daniel's smile held a hint of mild exasperation. 'My treat,' he added firmly.

'Sausage and chips!' Robbie declared. 'Can I have sausage and chips when we go to the pub?' He glanced across at his mother and saw her frown. 'Ple-e-ease,' he added, grinning up at Daniel. 'It's my favourite.'

'You can have anything you like, young man!'

'Ice-cream?' Robbie added hopefully. 'With chocolate sauce?'

'That too.'

Robbie's young face was a picture of delight. 'Great!'

'Thank you.'

Cathy's expression was serious. It was as if she had the weight of the world on her young shoulders, Daniel thought. To make her laugh—that would be his mission today. To remove that anxious frown from her oh, so beautiful face...

Seeing her smile was like winning a prize, and he *was* winning. An achievement had never felt so good. Their visit to the junk store had been a wash-out—piles of cheap, old-fashioned furniture for as far as the eye could see—but the rest of the day had made up for that.

The three of them had walked and joked and run and chased and it couldn't have felt any better than it did now—at least... Daniel's mouth curved ruefully as he mentally amended that last statement. There had been several points during the day when he had longed to take Cathy in his arms, to hold her and touch her and kiss her beautiful mouth...

'What are you smiling about?'

She sounded wonderful, Daniel thought, so happy and relaxed, the dulcet tones at their most attractive. 'Just thinking what a successful day it's been.' He looked across and smiled. 'Have you enjoyed it?'

Cathy raised her eyebrows in amused fashion. 'Did Robbie have second helpings for everything at the pub? It looked for all the world like I don't feed him properly! Yes, I've enjoyed it,' she added, smiling warmly. 'Very much.'

They were walking through the village, via a back lane

which Cathy would never have found had she been on her own. They turned a corner and a beautiful thatched cottage came into view. 'It's just like in a picture book, isn't it?' she murmured, gasping aloud. 'Oh, look!' she added excitedly. 'There's a little stream which runs all the way along.' She turned, bright-eyed, towards Daniel. 'It's beautiful here!' She inhaled a deep breath. 'Mmmm…smell that air. And it's *so* peaceful. When I think what it was like at the flat…' Her voice trailed away as she looked around at her surroundings. 'When I see all this, I *know* I've done the right thing; I just know it! Oh, the rent's extortionately high, but it's worth it, isn't it?' She spread her hands wide. 'To have all this on your doorstep… You know, I simply can't believe I'm living here. Oh, I know the house isn't in the best condition, and it isn't mine or anything, but even so…' She paused, aware that the two glasses of white wine which she had had at lunch had definitely loosened her tongue. 'If you could have seen the place Robbie and I escaped from!'

'Escaped?' A line creased Daniel's forehead. 'You make it sound like a prison. Was it really that bad?'

'Bad enough. A high-rise. The sort of building you see on television when they really want to depress the audience. I had good friends, though…' Cathy paused to smell a sprig of early honeysuckle. 'They're the only thing I miss.'

'The man who helped you move?'

Cathy glanced up. 'Gary?' She nodded, although Daniel detected an element of hesitation in her gaze. 'Yes.' A shutter fell over her expression for a moment, then she was on the move again. 'Oh, wow! Look over there!' She pointed through a gap in the hedgerow on the other side of the lane. 'Isn't that just the most incredible place? What's it called?'

Daniel didn't bother to look. He had forgotten that the house could be seen from here—at least at this time of the year, when the leaves were still not fully unfurled from their buds. 'Langforde Hall.'

'Can you *imagine* living somewhere as grand as that?'
Cathy turned to Daniel with laughing eyes. 'How incredible! It's nearly as big as a castle!'

Here it was, then, Daniel told himself, the perfect opportunity. 'Actually—'

'It's almost obscene, isn't it?' she continued. 'That a
place like that should house just one family. It does, I suppose? It hasn't been turned into apartments or anything?'

'Not yet.' Daniel's mouth twisted. 'You think it should
be?'

He watched as Cathy considered the creamy Georgian
mansion more carefully. 'No, it would ruin it, wouldn't it?
It's a beautiful building.' She smiled. 'Take no notice of
me, I'm just jealous!' she added light-heartedly. 'Robbie!'
Cathy's voice rose in alarm as he slipped his hand from
her hold in order to investigate the edge of the stream. 'For
goodness' sake, what on earth do you think you're doing?
Have you forgotten what happened on the village green?'
she scolded.

Obscene? Daniel glanced towards his family home as
Cathy reminded Robbie about the danger of going too near
water. Was that how she really saw it?

'I want to show you my place.' Daniel caught her hand
suddenly. He had been building towards this first step ever
since they had left the village pub. 'Come on, let's go inside.'

Cathy gazed up at the thatched cottage, her eyes scanning
the ancient tiled roof and tiny windows. 'Here? You live
here?' she repeated in amazement. 'But this is…amazing.'
She turned and looked at Daniel and he nodded in confir-
mation. 'I had no idea.' She smiled, shaking her head in
something approaching disbelief. 'How wonderful.' She
looked up at the building again. 'It's so…' She shook her
head. 'It must be very old,' she added finally.

'Three hundred years.' He pushed open the rickety garden gate and stood aside to allow her entry.

'I had no idea.'

Daniel focused on Cathy's expressive eyes and saw her uncertainties. 'About what?' he asked quietly.

'I...I thought you were...' she lifted her shoulders in an embarrassed shrug and he knew that she was finding the whole situation difficult '...a struggling artist.'

'Oh, I'm certainly that,' Daniel replied honestly. If she finds this difficult to take in, he thought, as they walked up the garden path edged with lavender, then what will she make of the rest of it? He inserted a key into the heavy front door. 'Come and have a look round.'

'It's lovely!' Cathy murmured as she stepped over the threshold. 'And so spacious...' she added, glancing around the interior, which wasn't quaint and olde worlde, as she had half expected, but open and light, with a few well-chosen pieces of furniture and practically no unnecessary clutter. She glanced at Daniel, a look of puzzled disbelief marring her expression. 'I had no idea,' she repeated.

'Are you rich?' Robbie had discovered a collection of wooden puzzles arranged on a side table and begun playing with them. 'You must be to have a house like this!'

'Robbie!' A tide of heat flooded Cathy's face. 'Don't speak like that!'

'Actually, I was left this house by my aunt,' Daniel replied, as evenly as he could.

'Really?' Cathy's eyes were wide with interest.

'Really.' He walked through to the kitchen, relieved that he hadn't had to lie about that at least. 'She died a couple of years ago and left me everything,' he explained. 'Lock, stock and barrel.'

'Well!' Cathy leant against a solid oak kitchen cabinet and smiled. 'You must have been *so* pleased—not that she died, of course,' she amended swiftly. 'But...well, you know. This is a wonderful house. You didn't really need anything at the junk store, did you?'

Daniel smiled ruefully. 'No, not really. It was an experience, though,' he added. 'I'll certainly keep it in mind for the future.'

Cathy looked around the kitchen. 'Was the house pretty much as it is now?'

'I cleared out a fair amount of furniture,' Daniel told her. 'My aunt was rather a hoarder. I don't think she threw anything away. Some of the stuff was junk, some quite valuable. What I didn't keep I sold.'

'Have we got an aunt who could leave us a house like this?' Robbie asked as he entered the kitchen.

Cathy smiled. 'I wish we had.'

'Can't we find one?' Robbie scrambled up onto a stool.

'Not quite as easy as that, darling,' Cathy replied cheerfully. 'My parents didn't have any brothers or sisters, and if they had...' She lifted her shoulders in a shrug.

'What about my daddy? Didn't he have anyone?'

Silence filled the room. 'Umm...no.' Cathy inhaled a steadying breath. 'No, actually, he didn't.' She knew her voice sounded shaky, but there was little she could do about it. Robbie had never asked about his father before. Of all the times to do so...

Cathy glanced across towards Daniel and saw that he was watching her. 'Can I help with anything?' she asked brightly.

'Nothing much to do.' Daniel smiled and held out a newly opened packet of chocolate digestives. 'Biscuit, Robbie?'

'Yeah, great!'

Cathy watched her son fall upon them as if he had been offered treasure. 'Why don't you take the packet and continue working on those puzzles?' Daniel suggested. 'I'll bring you a drink in a moment.' He waited until Robbie had left the room, then added gently, 'I take it, from the look on your face, that Robbie's never asked about his father before?'

Cathy watched Robbie as he carried his biscuits through to the other room. 'Is he all right eating in there?' she asked. 'I don't want him to ruin anything.'

'He's fine.' Daniel's dark gaze never left Cathy's face. 'Robbie and his father?' he repeated.

'I don't know what to say.' Cathy lifted her shoulders in an awkward shrug. She shook her head and her striking mane of auburn hair glinted in the sunshine. 'He's never been a part of Robbie's life.'

'He was once a part of yours.'

She nodded reluctantly. 'Yes.'

'For how long?'

'Daniel…' There was a note of desperation in Cathy's voice. 'I don't want to talk about this—not right now.'

'You think I'm prying,' he murmured quietly.

'No. No, it's not that. I just really don't think I can talk about him…' Cathy shook her head, inhaled a massive breath. 'I…I get too upset.'

Daniel frowned. 'He hurt you that much?'

'Please! Can we just change the subject?' Cathy moved jerkily to the kitchen table and picked up a mug of coffee. She took a mouthful, then said stiltedly, 'Is it a strain keeping up with the running costs of this place?'

'A strain?' Daniel made an effort to gather his thoughts. 'No…no, I live pretty frugally. Don't go in for fancy food, never been particularly keen on overheated houses…' His mouth curved, but the light in his smile didn't reach his eyes. He should just tell her now and get it over and done with. Why was he finding it so difficult? Why?

Daniel looked into Cathy's sweet face and tried to analyse his feelings. Fear, that was what it all boiled down to. Fear of losing her. He knew, with more certainty than he knew anything, that as soon as he revealed the extent of his wealth, his so called 'position' in the village, things would change. This woman was fragile, proud, defensive about her lack of money. She would look at the differences between them and think they were too wide, too vast. He didn't want that. He didn't want anything to spoil this wonderful beginning.

'Oh, you must just love coming over to my place, then!'

Cathy replied ebulliently. 'I really cannot fathom out the state of my plumbing at all! I'm very pleased for you,' she murmured, casting appreciative eyes around the expensively fitted kitchen. 'It's a wonderful old house.'

'Thank you.' His dark brown eyes were steady on her face. 'You know, Cathy, you really are a pretty remarkable woman.'

'That's one way of putting it, I suppose!'

'Do you always do this?' His gaze was watchful.

Cathy blushed. 'Do what?'

'Refuse to accept compliments when they come your way.'

'No one has ever really...' She shook her head, smiled into his eyes. 'You're the first person to say... I'm just an ordinary girl,' she murmured, 'living an ordinary life.'

'Hardly that.' He saw the warmth which was suffusing her skin. Had anyone ever done this before? he wondered. Taken the trouble to get under her skin, pushed and probed, bothered to ask questions? 'Let's go through to the sitting room.' Daniel picked up the tray of coffee and led the way to an alcove where two chairs were positioned to make the most of the views of the countryside. He released a heavy breath as they took their seats, watched her for a moment, then said, 'Will you and Robbie stay for dinner?'

'Dinner...?' She smiled through the tears and his heart was warm, because she looked so pleased, so surprised, so darned *grateful*.

'Don't say no,' he warned, watching her changing expression as doubts and uncertainties began to creep in. 'I won't hear of it. Do you like steak?' His mouth twisted into a stunning smile. 'I'm not blowing my own trumpet or anything, but I can do this incredible feat of brilliance with cream and mushrooms and a dash of Worcester sauce which fools people into thinking I'm a gourmet chef.'

'Sounds gorgeous!' The intensity of her smile took his

breath away. 'Are you sure you want to go to all the trouble?'

'It's no trouble.' Daniel assured her quietly, looking deep into her eyes. 'Believe me…'

CHAPTER SIX

'THAT was dee-licious!' Robbie put his elbows on the table and rested his chin in his hands. 'Is there ice-cream for pudding?'

Daniel smiled. 'No ice-cream, I'm afraid. Only frozen yoghurt.'

'Ugh! What's that?'

'Just what it says,' Cathy remarked mildly. 'Why don't you try some and find out?'

Robbie considered for a moment. 'OK,' he replied lightly.

Cathy stood up and began gathering the used dishes. 'I'll do this.'

'No, you won't.' Daniel picked up Robbie's empty plate and winked. 'My house; I'm in charge.'

'But it's no trouble. And besides, you cooked,' Cathy argued. She was worried about the expense of the meal—the steaks had been large and juicy and must have cost fortune. She wondered briefly whether Daniel had bought them as some sort of celebration—perhaps he'd sold one of his paintings—or whether he frequently had food of that calibre lurking in his refrigerator.

'Daniel's house.' Robbie repeated, eyes twinkling. 'You've got to do what you're told!'

'There you are, you see?' Daniel's mouth curved in amusement. 'Even Robbie can see the logic. You're my guest,' he added, his voice firm as he glanced down into Cathy's weary face. 'I insist.'

'Nobody ever tells Mummy what to do,' Robbie remarked gleefully. 'But she's always bossing me about!'

'Just for that remark you can help Daniel clear away!'

Cathy replied, with a light-hearted smile. 'Go on!' she instructed, when Robbie pulled a face.

'You can come and find out what flavour yoghurts I've got in the freezer,' Daniel suggested. 'Cathy, what about you?'

'None for me, thanks.'

'How about coffee?'

'Mmm, that would be nice. Are you sure I can't help?'

Daniel threw her a mild look. 'What do you think?'

She didn't argue. She was too tired for that. Pleasantly so, relaxed and warm and happy, but tired nonetheless.

The dinner had been a great success. Robbie hadn't got bored—Daniel had made sure to include him in all the conversation—and he had liked the food. Quite a feat, given his usual favourites of fishfingers and chips, she thought.

She stifled a huge yawn. The dining area was cosy and snug, tucked away in an alcove off the large sitting room. Cathy found herself staring in hypnotic fashion towards the large open fire. It was barely seven o'clock—they had eaten early for Robbie's sake—but the clear skies of the afternoon had clouded over and it was becoming quite dark outside.

'We'll have to be going soon,' Cathy murmured, as Daniel and Robbie, holding a dish carefully in his hands, returned from the kitchen.

'Oh Mum!' Robbie sounded disgusted.

'Well, we will.' Cathy glanced into Daniel's face. 'The Land Rover is still in the pub car park,' she reminded him. 'We're going to have to walk.'

'No, it's OK.' Daniel placed the tray he was carrying down onto the polished wooden table. 'I can drive you back.'

Cathy frowned. 'How?'

He hesitated, realising his mistake. Another opportunity, he told himself. Why not just confess that the brand-new Jaguar she supposed had been returned to its rightful owner was in fact parked in the garage beside the house and was his? He imagined himself doing just that, and knew with the utmost certainty that the relaxed expression, so wonderful to see on her beautiful face now, would change in an instant to one of tense disbelief.

'I've got a pushbike.' The words were out before he could stop them. He frowned slightly. He did have one—somewhere. 'I can ride over in a couple of minutes and fetch the Land Rover, then drive it back here.'

'Oh.' Cathy frowned. 'Are you're sure you don't mind?'

'Why should I mind?'

'Well…you've gone to so much trouble for us today: taking us out to lunch, cooking a great dinner—'

'It's been a pleasure.' His voice was low, husky with conviction. He lifted a hand and gently held her face. His mouth, for a second so serious, whispered the hint of a smile. 'Why should I mind?' he repeated, and in the next moment he was lowering his head to kiss her.

He melted as his mouth brushed her lips, closed his eyes, completely lost in the moment. He had never imagined that wanting someone would be this exhilarating, this intense.

'Ooooh! You're kissing!'

Cathy jerked her head away, and he was aware of the rush of heat which flooded up from her neck into her face. She looked troubled, her eyes flitting towards Robbie, who was sitting opposite, grinning at both of them. Daniel winked.

'Do you like my mummy?' Robbie carefully spooned pink yoghurt into his mouth. 'She likes you; I know she does. She never used to look in the mirror, and now she does it all the time!' He raised his brows and rolled brown eyes in a comical fashion. 'She keeps brushing her hair, and now she's started putting that black stuff on her eyes.'

'Robbie!' Cathy's face was like a furnace. 'You rotten devil! How could you say that?'

He giggled. 'And she definitely would like you to come round and visit us—every day if you like,' Robbie added, looking at Daniel with a hopeful expression.

'Now Robbie—!' Cathy began.

'It's OK.' Daniel looked amused. 'I like hearing this sort of talk; it's doing wonders for my ego. Every day?' Daniel raised dark brows and pretended to give it some consideration. 'Well, it might be a little difficult sometimes, but I'll certainly see what I can do.' He winked. 'Every day, huh? I'm doing pretty good, then, am I?'

'Oh, yes!' Robbie nodded his head vigorously. 'Very good indeed!'

'Shall we take our coffee through into the sitting room?' Daniel suggested, with a wicked wink at Cathy this time. 'It will be more comfortable.'

'He likes you.' Cathy took a sip of coffee. 'I've never seen him this relaxed with—' She halted abruptly.

'With a stranger?' Daniel queried gently. 'It's OK, go ahead and say it; I won't be offended.'

'You're more than a stranger,' she murmured.

Daniel's gaze was intense suddenly. 'I hope so.' He paused. 'I know what I'd like to be...'

They had had wine with the meal: a bottle of burgundy which had tasted like nectar even to Cathy's unsophisticated palate. The effects of the alcohol were certainly helping her to cope with moments like these, she thought. No tension or disbelief on hearing such a statement, just a warm, hopeful glow, which burned brightly inside.

'Oh!' A wash of desire swept over her. She wasn't used to this. Was desperation making her believe things that simply couldn't be true? She wanted him to want her *so* much. Was that bad? she wondered. It didn't feel bad. Was it foolish? Probably. And dangerous. Because she knew, she just *knew* she would end up hurting.

'Don't sound so surprised.' His mouth curved into a wry smile. 'I haven't exactly gone out of my way to hide how I feel, have I?'

'I'm just...' Cathy bit down on her bottom lip. 'But yesterday evening...?'

'What about it?'

'I thought...' Cathy shook her head and frowned. 'Are you sure? You haven't had too much to drink, have you?' she asked in all seriousness. 'Because if you have, I'll understand—'

'I'm stone-cold sober. I've had one glass of wine all evening. Cathy, you are truly amazing. Why is it so difficult to believe that I could find you attractive?'

'Because...because this sort of thing doesn't happen to the likes of me, that's all.'

'The likes of you?' Daniel's mouth twisted. 'What do you mean?'

'You could have any woman you want,' Cathy murmured softly. 'You're handsome and kind, and funny and smart—Sandra's crazy about you.'

'Sandra?' Daniel frowned. 'What on earth has Sandra got to do with anything? Cathy, for heaven's sake, why do you do this to yourself? Why so negative and self-deprecating?'

'I'm just being realistic!'

'Cathy, you are a clever, determined, beautiful woman,' Daniel asserted softly.

'I...I don't know what to say,' she murmured.

'You don't have to say anything.' His eyes looked darker than she had ever seen them before. Such gorgeous eyes, Cathy thought. So wonderfully intense. Magic eyes. Because as she looked into his face she believed every word, every unspoken message.

'Daniel, help me build this. Ple-e-ease!' Robbie tugged gently on the sleeve of his jumper. 'I can't make the bricks stand up.'

'Can you not?' Daniel turned from the table. She looked for signs of irritation in his expression but saw none, and her heart warmed. 'Ah, now that's a tricky one. You need to put this one here...'

Cathy watched them as they worked at the puzzles together. Robbie was lying full-length on the rug in front of the fire, with Daniel crouched beside him. They were chatting companionably, in low, soothing murmurs. She settled

her head back against the sofa, curling her legs up underneath her. It was wonderful to be able to relax like this.
She thought about Daniel's words, the way he had looked
at her just now. She couldn't understand it, but that didn't
make it less true. Don't try to analyse any of it, she told
herself. This *is* happening. You're not dreaming. He wants
you.

'Hey!' Robbie's expressive face lit up with glee.
'Mummy's asleep.'

'Looks like it.' Daniel glanced across at Cathy and his
mouth curved into a gentle smile. 'She must have been very
tired.'

Robbie nodded. 'Oh, yes. My mummy works very hard.
When we lived with Grandma she used to go out to work
at the supermarket every night. She was always tired then.'

Daniel raised dark brows. 'Every night?'

Robbie nodded. 'I used to sleep in the big bed with
Grandma.'

'Shall we keep quiet, so that Mummy can sleep?' Daniel
suggested. He glanced at his wristwatch. 'Hey, do you
know what the time is? I didn't realise we'd been playing
this game for so long. It's almost eight o'clock. When's
your bedtime?'

'Oh, not for ages and ages!' Robbie stifled a yawn. 'I
can go to bed whenever I like!'

'Really?'

'Yes. I can stay up till *midnight* if I want. Of course,'
Robbie went on artlessly, 'I usually have a glass of milk
and some biscuits about this time. Chocolate ones, like before,' he added hopefully.

'Sounds a good idea.' Daniel got to his feet. 'I'll get us
both a drink.'

'What about Mummy?'

Daniel glanced down into Cathy's sleeping face. 'We'll
leave her for a little while longer, shall we? As she looks
so peaceful.'

'Good idea.' Robbie nodded his head sagely. 'Mummies need all the rest they can get.'

When Daniel returned with the milk and a plateful of chocolate biscuits a few minutes later, as requested, he found Robbie lying full-length on the rug, sound asleep.

He placed the milk and biscuits onto a side table, then after a moment's consideration knelt down and scooped Robbie into his arms.

The smallest guest bedroom seemed appropriate. It was cosy and snug, decorated in cream and blue, with a patch-work quilt and a wooden sailing boat on a chest beneath the eaves which Daniel had had since he was a child.

Daniel pulled back the covers of the bed with one hand and laid the boy down gently onto the sheets, conscious of the novelty of the situation. He eased off the boy's shoes, then pulled the coverlet over Robbie's slender body.

Cathy was still sleeping soundly when he went back into the sitting room. He knelt down beside the chair and looked into her face. He shook his head, almost bemused by the feelings she aroused in him: tenderness, the need to pro-tect—passion. When had he ever felt this strongly? He thought of all the women in his past. Enough of a cross-section to know that he had never experienced anything like this before. Was it love? He frowned. Was this what hap-pened? Did it spring up and hit you on the head when you were least expecting it?

'I wondered where you were.'

She looked like a little girl: tousled hair, sleepy eyes. Daniel put his paintbrush down and smiled. 'Well, now you've found me.' He glanced at the work in front of him, then covered the easel with a sheet. 'Sleep OK?'

'I'm sorry about that. I didn't...' Cathy shook her head. She dragged a hand through her messed-up hair. 'I'm be-ginning to make a habit of falling asleep at inappropriate moments, aren't I?'

'Clearly my company isn't as riveting as I had hoped it might be—!'

'Oh, no!' She looked concerned. 'I didn't mean—!'

Daniel smiled, eyes sparkling in Cathy's direction. 'Joke. It wasn't inappropriate as far as I was concerned,' he added. 'You obviously needed the rest.' He switched the light off in his studio and walked toward the doorway. 'You and Robbie are quite a pair.'

'Where is he?' A frown creased Cathy's forehead. 'I saw this light…I thought he'd be with you.'

'Don't worry. Robbie's fine. He's in here.' Daniel led the way along the landing to the smallest bedroom. He stood aside to allow Cathy to enter the room. The light from the hallway illuminated Robbie's angelic face. 'He fell asleep on the rug. I thought he'd be more comfortable in here.'

'Isn't he the sweetest darling?' Cathy murmured lovingly. She glanced back at Daniel with a wry smile. 'Of course I'm biased.' She bent and kissed Robbie tenderly on the cheek. 'It seems a shame to wake him,' she murmured.

'Do we have to?'

'Oh, he'll sleep for hours now.' She glanced at her watch. 'It's way past his bedtime.'

'Which is precisely why it would be better if we left him until morning.'

'You mean…he should stay?'

'Not just Robbie. You too.' His mouth curved into an easy, attractive smile. 'Why not?'

'Well…because…' Cathy struggled to think of a suitable reason. She looked into Daniel's face, was aware, as never before, of the rugged masculinity of his frame. 'It's getting late.'

'You'll have to do better than that.' Daniel's eyes were steady on Cathy's face. 'That's a reason to stay, not to go.' He took a step towards her, brushed her cheek with his hand. His voice was warm and reassuring. 'Forget about any preconceived ideas you may have and just relax. The last thing I want to do is pressurise you into something you're not ready for.'

'Really?'

'Really.' Her eyes were large and very beautiful. 'Come and have a look at the bathroom.' He took her hand in his and led the way along the landing. 'Believe it or not, but this house has magnificent plumbing; there's lots of hot water and I do a good line in thick fluffy towels.' Daniel opened a door and pulled the light switch. 'What do you think?'

Cathy sighed, her eyes scanning the well-designed room with its pristine white tiles and pretty lemon wallpaper. 'If you're trying to tempt me, then you're doing a good job,' she murmured lightly. She released a sigh. 'This is gorgeous. I've never bathed in a corner bath before.'

'Well, now's your chance.' Daniel looked at her and his expression was light. This was the way he must play it, he told himself: casual, easy. He could practically feel the rigidity of her body next to his. 'Better make the most of it—I don't offer everyone this opportunity!

'Cathy...' Daniel's voice was husky with feeling. He held himself in check, conscious of the desire spiralling through his body. There had been too many times in the past when he'd not taken the time to think about the consequences of his actions. She looked so...fragile, so unneccessarily anguished. 'Please don't read anything more into the situation than you need to. There's no hidden agenda. I just want you to have a relaxing, restful evening.' Fine words, he thought, and he *did* mean them, he really did, but following his principles through wasn't going to be quite so easy...

Cathy sat on the bath stool and poured a measure of perfumed bath oil into the running hot water. She smiled to herself. Daniel was perfect. He understood. She had never met anyone like him before. This *is* happening, she told

herself. You aren't dreaming. There are men in the world
who are honest and decent and who care.

She emerged from the bathroom wrapped in a large bath-
robe almost an hour later. She stuck her head around the
smallest bedroom to check that Robbie was still fast asleep,
then went in search of Daniel.

She walked into the sitting room before realising that the
front door, which opened straight into the room, was open.
Daniel was talking to someone. Cathy glanced across, saw
an all too familiar face, and quickly dodged out of eye line.

Too late. Sandra had seen her. For a split second their
eyes met. Cathy frowned, conscious of how things must
look. What should she do? Damn! Sandra had seen her and
was bound to jump to the wrong conclusion.

Cathy stood in front of the fire, twisting the tie of the
robe between anxious fingers. She tried not to eavesdrop,
but it was difficult...

'Well, I really must be going. I can see you have company.' A significant pause. 'I hope you didn't mind my
asking, Daniel, only we do live in modern times and I
thought... Well, I think you know what I thought. A girl
can't help but try!' Sandra's dulcet tones sounded more
than a little strained. 'Of course I had no idea that you
wouldn't be attending this year...'

'Not at all.' Daniel's reply was smooth and assured. 'And
as for you being a modern girl, Sandra, I don't think that
was ever in doubt.'

'Er...perhaps we could get together another time—for a
drink or something?'

'Perhaps.'

Cathy looked across at Daniel. His body language said
it all; there didn't seem to be an ounce of tension in the
whole of his frame.

'Good bath?' Daniel closed the door a moment later.
Cathy watched as he came towards her. She hadn't
been mistaken; he didn't seem the least bit perturbed by
Sandra's call.

'Yes, thank you. It was lovely.' She tried her hardest to appear composed. 'She saw me.'

'Who?' He frowned, then glanced back towards the front door. 'Oh, you mean Sandra. Did she?'

'You're not concerned?'

His mouth twisted into a relaxed smile. 'Why should I be concerned?'

'She's bound to think…' Cathy glanced down at the robe she wore and heaved a breath. 'From the way I'm dressed she's definitely going to jump to the wrong conclusion.'

Daniel raised an enquiring eyebrow. 'And you mind about that?'

His voice was mild, but Cathy detected a steely undertone. She looked into his tanned handsome face. 'It was just a shock, that's all. I—'

'Do you mind?' he repeated quietly.

'I don't know! I told you, I'm not used—' Cathy shook her head a little. 'What did she want?'

'Oh…nothing much.' Daniel ran a hand through his glossy hair. He seemed to be having trouble concentrating, Cathy thought. 'She was just asking about…the ball. You remember we saw a poster for it earlier this afternoon outside the pub?'

'Yes…?' Cathy could barely concentrate either; her heart was racing wildly inside her chest.

'She asked if I'd partner her.' He looked faintly amused.

'Oh!' Cathy swallowed. 'And will you?'

Daniel shook his head, glancing at Cathy as if she had asked a faintly ridiculous question. 'No, Sandra would be the last person I'd want at my side. Besides, I'm not going to be around for the ball this year. And if I were…well, let's just say it's not my most favourite example of an evening's entertainment. Come over here.' He took Cathy by the hand and led her over to one of the large cream sofas which filled the living room. 'Now, I don't want to talk about Sandra, or the ball; I only want to talk about you.'

He looked deep into her eyes, hesitated a moment, then said gently, 'Tell me about Robbie's father.'

'He's dead,' Cathy murmured after a moment. She looked into Daniel's face with misted eyes. 'So...' she shook her head, determined to be strong '...there's really nothing more to say on the subject. He's gone. He can't...he can't—'

'Hurt you any more—is that what you were going to say?' Daniel asked gently.

Cathy nodded. She saw Daniel's eyes darken, his jaw clench. It felt good, she realised, to have someone who seemed to feel so strongly on her behalf. 'Does Robbie know?'

'Yes. I told him... Well, the basic truth—that his father died before he was born.'

'Before?' Daniel frowned. 'That must have been very difficult.'

'Yes, yes, it was.' Cathy inhaled a ragged breath. 'But not for the reasons you're imagining.' She shook her head. 'If you're expecting a tale of tragic young love, then you're in for a disappointment!' She knew her voice sounded hard. 'I was young and naive and foolish,' she murmured, anguished by the memories. 'One night. That's all it took...'

She pressed her lips together in a firm line. She hadn't planned on this, on spilling out her past mistakes to Daniel, but now she had begun it felt like the right thing to do. 'He was drinking heavily—vodka, I think, or gin...something like that. I don't like the taste of spirits, so I stuck to orange juice, but he...' Cathy looked into the fire. The flames were mesmerising. She thought back to the night when Robbie had been conceived. 'I didn't realise until afterwards, but he had been putting vodka into my drink all evening. I couldn't understand what was happening. Later...when he began...' Cathy placed a hand over her eyes. 'I never expected him to do that to me. I wanted my first time to be special...' She was quiet for a long moment, then she looked at Daniel, eyes wide with hurt. 'Was your first time special?'

'Not particularly, no.' Daniel's voice was deep and soothing. 'Memorable, perhaps, but for all the wrong reasons; I was too young and too drunk and I didn't have a clue.' He touched her face with the edge of his finger. 'But we're not talking about me, we're talking about you.' He paused. 'What happened next?'

'Afterwards…when I knew I was pregnant, he…he didn't want to know. He said…' Cathy sniffed, remembering the hurt and the pain. 'He said that getting drunk was the only way he could bring himself to…to make love to me. I was fatter then,' she added, by way of explanation, 'even more awful-looking than I am now. He was *so* horrible.' Cathy risked a glance across at Daniel. There was steel in his expression. 'You look fierce.'

'Do you blame me?' Daniel's eyes never left Cathy's face.

'I know what you're thinking,' she continued swiftly. 'Why did I ever waste my time on someone like that?' She shook her head. 'And the truth is, I just don't know.' Her voice was little more than a whisper. 'My self-esteem's never been particularly high. I suppose I was…grateful that he took notice of me. I know it sounds pathetic now,' she continued in stronger tones, 'but I was just seventeen. I hadn't discovered who I was, or what I wanted out of life, and I had absolutely no experience with men—still haven't,' she added, with a small smile. 'Steve undermined my confidence all the time. I didn't think about it whilst we were together, but later, when he was gone, when I had chance to reflect on everything…'

'How did he die?'

'A car accident.' Cathy's voice was flat. 'After he told me he didn't care about the baby he began stealing cars with his mates, going for joy-rides around the estate. Actually, I think he'd always been doing it, but it became more obvious then. They say he was doing almost sixty miles an hour when he collided with a parked car.'

'And Robbie knows absolutely nothing about his father?'

'No. I used to have a photograph, but I'm afraid I destroyed it on the day he told me to "Get down the clinic and have an abortion or something".'

Daniel frowned. 'That's what he said?'

'That and more besides.' Cathy's smile was weak. 'But you wouldn't want to hear the rest. That's why I've never told Robbie anything. How do you tell a child that his own father didn't want him? I've gone over it so many times, tried hard to do what was for the best. Of course, I blame myself for getting involved with him in the first place—'

'But if you hadn't then you wouldn't have Robbie now, would you? He's the proof that good things can come from bad,' Daniel asserted gently.

'Yes.' Cathy's eyes shone with tears. 'He means everything...the whole world to me.'

'That much is obvious.' Daniel raised a hand and cupped Cathy's face. His dark eyes gleamed with sympathy. 'You look tired.'

'I am.' Cathy wanted to sink against his strong, masculine body. His touch felt *so* good, so warm and powerful. 'I seem to have felt tired for ages,' she murmured. 'I guess this move has taken more out of me than I realised.'

'Bed?' Daniel's smile was gentle. 'Don't blush. I've got some work to do. You can use my room. I'll sleep in my study.'

Cathy hesitated. 'Are...are you sure?'

The lie didn't come easily to his lips. 'Absolutely.'

She placed a light hand on his. 'If you only knew how much I appreciate the way you're treating me. I know I'm a silly, mixed-up, foolish girl, but—'

'Who said anything about silly or foolish?' Daniel's voice was firm. 'You've had a hard time. You feel vulnerable—'

'I don't want to feel vulnerable. I want to feel bold and adventurous!' Cathy replied.

'Sounds interesting.' His mouth curved into a gloriously

attractive smile. 'Hey!' He frowned, wiping the edge of his thumb gently across her cheek. 'Cathy, don't cry, sweetheart. What's there to cry about?'

'I'm just so...so...' She shook her head in annoyance, momentarily lost for words.

'Beautiful? Courageous?'

'Don't joke!' Cathy jerked away from his touch and wiped her eyes. 'Pathetic,' she added forcibly. 'That's what I am, pathetic!'

'You are not pathetic.' He held her by the shoulders and turned her towards him again. 'Don't say that. You are a courageous, beautiful woman who's had a difficult few years and needs life to be more kind to her.'

'I'm a coward.'

'Why?'

'You know why,' Cathy murmured awkwardly. 'Any other woman—'

'Because you don't want to sleep with me?' Daniel sounded genuinely amazed. 'Cathy, don't beat yourself up like this. I can be a patient guy.' His mouth twisted into a smile. 'OK, so patience isn't a particular forte, but where you're concerned I'm prepared to work hard at doing what's right.'

'Why are you...?' Cathy pressed her lips together. 'Why are you being like this? I'm so...' She shook her head, glanced towards the door. 'Perhaps it's best if I leave.'

'Is that what you want?' He was still holding her. Dark, sensuous eyes mesmerised her face. 'If you do, then I will take you home. Believe me, Cathy,' he added seriously, 'when I say that what you want takes precedence over everything else.' Daniel thought of his own needs and desires and thrust them to the back of his mind, 'Everything,' he repeated. He tilted her chin with his finger and forced her to look into his face. Hell! This was so difficult. He hardly knew where his will-power was coming from. 'Besides, I've got work to do,' he added with a smile. He knew his words sounded slightly strangulated. He wondered if Cathy realised how much restraint he was having to employ.

'What sort of work?' she queried. 'Painting, do you mean?'

'Painting…?' Daniel struggled to gather his thoughts. 'No, not painting. At least…' Later, he promised himself. He would enjoy working on a portrait again. 'No… paperwork.' Cathy frowned slightly. 'I'm involved with a couple of charities,' he explained. 'It's something I do from time to time.'

'Oh, I see.' She smiled. 'You really are a good samaritan, aren't you?'

'Just call me St Daniel of Langforde!' he quipped. She was too close, and she smelt wonderful, of honeysuckle and wild roses. It wasn't helping his resolutions any. Daniel released his hold. 'I'll show you to my room,' he added somewhat abruptly. 'You'll be just across the hall from Robbie.'

He made it easy on them both by maintaining a suitable distance: not crossing the threshold, not touching her. 'I'll be in my study if you need anything,' he told her.

'Thanks.' Cathy caught his arm as he turned away. 'Daniel…' Her expression made it all worthwhile: so sweet, so full of gratitude. 'Thank you.'

'My pleasure,' he murmured huskily. And found to his own amazement, given the depth of his desire, the need which was coursing through his veins, that he actually meant it.

CHAPTER SEVEN

DANIEL scraped off a little paint with his palette knife, added an important touch of deepest red to the shock of hair which dominated a great proportion of the portrait, then stood back to assess his work so far; he had set out to capture Cathy's innocence and vulnerability on canvas and that was what he felt he had achieved.

He continued to gaze critically at the painting; it was a strong piece of work, probably his finest to date. Daniel released a breath which signified a little of the emotion within him. He felt different, alive with the possibilities of what lay ahead. There was no doubt Cathy brought out the best in him. He just hoped this wonderful, almost crazy phenomenon was a two-way thing.

Daniel eased a hand across his aching neck, glanced at his wristwatch and saw with surprise that it was almost three in the morning. His work on the Langforde Charity Foundation had taken longer than he'd thought, and then, as was often the way, he had become so engrossed with his painting that he had lost track of time.

He heard a small snuffling sound, then what sounded like a sort of whimper. Daniel stood still for a moment and listened. There it was again, only louder this time. He placed his palette knife onto the small table behind him and wiped his hands clean on an oily cloth. He should investigate.

Robbie was still sleeping soundly. Daniel pulled the bedroom door closed and walked along the landing to his own bedroom.

Cathy looked hot and unhappy in sleep. Daniel leant an arm against the frame of the doorway, watching with concern as she tossed and turned in the large double bed, her arms flailing wildly. Light from the landing illuminated the tormented expression on her face. She cried out again, some mumbled, indecipherable words which tore at his heart, and he moved quickly into the room, closing the door behind him so that the noise wouldn't waken Robbie.

'Cathy…shh…sweetheart, it's just a dream…' He sat on the edge of the bed and placed gentle hands on her shoulders. 'Cathy…' he repeated gently. 'You're dreaming. Wake up…' She cried out again, seemingly lost in some personal nightmare, and Daniel leant low, lifting her body against his own to hold her close. 'Cathy…' He whispered her name gently, stroking back the damp strands of hair from her face. 'Sweetheart…it's all right…it's all right…'

She found herself awake and in his arms. She knew where she was; she knew that Daniel was holding her. She listened to the sound of his deep voice and closed her eyes, sinking softly against the strength of his body. It felt wonderful to be held like this. After the nightmare… Cathy squeezed her eyes tight shut. She didn't want to think about that now. She whimpered a little, despite the knowledge that Robbie was alive and safe, and sleeping soundly just along the hallway.

'Sweet darling….'

Daniel's voice was the most heartwarming thing she had ever heard. It melted her in the darkness. Cathy laid her head against his solid chest, conscious that there was just a layer of cotton between her cheek and his tanned skin. She raised her head a little. 'Daniel…it was a horrible dream. They took Robbie and I tried to find him, but everywhere I looked…' Cathy gulped a ragged breath. 'And there were these men with scars on their faces and claws for hands and—'

'Shh.' He held her close. 'Don't think about it any more. It isn't real. Robbie's safe…you're safe.'

'Yes…' Cathy inhaled another breath. The pure, masculine scent of Daniel was almost overwhelming, like an aphrodisiac in the darkness. 'Daniel…?'

'Yes?'

Cathy swallowed and lifted her head away from his chest, looking up at him in the soft moonlight. 'Will you…kiss me?' she asked.

Silence filled the room. For a moment Cathy thought he hadn't heard, or didn't want to, that she had made a terrible mistake, not to mention a complete and utter fool of herself. Then Daniel's head lowered, and in the next moment she felt the warmth of his mouth on hers…

His lips were soft and warm, full of slow, lingering tenderness. Cathy clung to him, parting her mouth, welcoming the feelings of desire as they surged through her body. She had never known such need, such a mixture of anticipation and excitement and ecstasy all rolled up into one. She moved her position a little, linking her arms up and around his neck, pressing closer, aware of the taut hardness of his body, of the thin layer of tee-shirt which kept their nakedness apart.

'Cathy…' Daniel's voice was husky with desire. She loved the rugged sound of it close against her skin, the feel of his powerful hands cradling her head. 'You're sure about this?'

'Mmm…' She seemed to have forgotten how to speak as his mouth trailed a path of kisses along the arch of her neck, down towards the base of her throat.

He laid her back against the bed. Cathy felt the coolness of the sheets beneath her heated skin. 'You know I wanted you from the very first moment, don't you?' Daniel asserted in deep, gravelly tones. He lifted himself from her, so that he could look deep into her eyes. 'There's something so special about you, Cathy. You take my breath away. You make me feel…' His dark head shook a little, as if he had no words to explain. 'Let me show you…' he murmured huskily.

*   *   *

It took Cathy some moments to work out where she was when she awoke next morning. She opened her eyes and found herself focusing on a pile of books and a tiny silver carriage clock which showed it was just past eight.

Then she remembered, and a thrill of excitement scorched through her body. She released a quivering breath. Last night had been the most wonderful night of her life. She had gone from ghoulish nightmare to beautiful dream. She remembered the way he had held her, touched her, cared for her. They had made love and it had been the most wonderful, spectacular, tender moment of her life…

She heard a familiar shout. Cathy threw back the bed-covers, grabbed the robe she had been wearing last night and padded across the room to peer out of the small latticed window.

She smiled. Robbie was outside in the garden, playing with a ball. Cathy sat on the window seat and watched her son as he scampered in and around a few rather neglected flowerbeds. 'Daniel!' He tilted his head back and yelled cheerfully. 'Come and play with me again, Daniel!'

Cathy opened the window. 'Robbie, shh! Stop yelling at the top of your voice.'

'Hello, Mummy.' Robbie's expression was full of fun. 'Daniel's been playing football with me.'

'Has he, darling?' Cathy smiled down at her son. 'Have you scored?'

'Oh, yes! Daniel showed me how to kick properly, and I'm much better now. You've been sleeping for a long time.' Robbie stated matter-of-factly. 'I wanted to come up ages ago, but Daniel said we should let you rest.'

'That was very kind of him—' There was a tap at the bedroom door. Cathy inhaled a steadying breath and ran a hand through her dishevelled hair. 'Come in!' she called.

Daniel entered. He looked wonderful, dressed in shorts and a close fitting tee-shirt which revealed a great deal of muscular tanned arm and leg. Cathy's heart did a back-flip. 'I thought you might like breakfast in your room.'

'Your room,' Cathy corrected him. She smiled, glancing at the tray he was carrying; there was a jug of freshly squeezed orange juice, a pot of coffee and a mound of hot, buttered toast. 'Looks delicious!' She smiled shyly. 'Thank you.'

'My pleasure.' Daniel placed the tray down onto the window seat beside her, then bent and kissed her mouth. 'It's going to be a beautiful day,' he murmured.

'Yes…' Cathy's smile was radiant beneath the warmth of his lips. 'I think it is…'

There was a boisterous shout from the garden below. Cathy dragged her gaze away from Daniel's face and glanced out of the window, watching as Robbie attempted to dribble the football around the garden. 'Was he up *very* early?' she murmured.

'Six o'clock.'

Cathy pulled a face. 'I'm afraid he's always been a bit of an early riser…' She glanced at him, remembering their hours of lovemaking last night. 'You haven't had much sleep, then?'

'Such a sacrifice.' He leant forward, cupped her cheek in his hand and kissed her mouth again. 'I got up early anyway. I wasn't sure how Robbie would feel if he found us together in bed.' He paused. 'After all my promises last night…'

'Yes…' Cathy frowned. 'Daniel…you don't *regret* what happened, do you?'

'How on earth could I do that?' His voice was soft. Dark eyes searched her face intently. 'And you—no regrets?'

'Oh, no!' Cathy released a taut breath and smiled. 'No,' she repeated. 'I still can't believe it happened, though.'

'It happened.' His gaze was full of rugged, male sexuality. Sensuous lips curved into a smile. 'More than once.' Daniel lifted the jug filled with orange juice and began to pour the golden liquid into two sparkling glasses. 'We should be drinking champagne,' he asserted, 'to celebrate.'

'If only.' Cathy sipped a mouthful of juice. 'I had a glass

of champagne once, but I didn't like it much,' she confided. 'It was dry and sharp and all the bubbles went up my nose and made me sneeze.'

'Doesn't sound too good.' Daniel smiled. 'There are others. Spend enough money and it really is a very special taste.'

'You sound like an expert.' Cathy smiled happily. 'So! What have you been doing with yourself this morning? Robbie says you taught him how to kick a football properly.'

'He'll make a pretty good player when he's older; he's got a good eye for the ball. We worked in my studio together too.'

'Painting?' Cathy enquired.

'Yes.' Daniel's lips curved. 'Robbie gave me his advice on a particular painting I'm working on. He had very strong views.'

'You are a saint, do you know that? Hardly any sleep, keeping my son occupied, bringing me breakfast—'

'I'm no saint.' His voice held a serious tone.

Cathy glanced across and saw the intense look in his eyes. 'No?' she queried softly.

'Not a bit of it.' Daniel took a step towards her. 'If you only knew—'

'Mummy, look what I've done!' Robbie scampered into the room at that moment, holding a large piece of paper. 'Daniel helped me mix the colours, but I did it all by myself.'

Cathy, conscious of the sensuous look in Daniel's eyes, somehow managed to drag her gaze away. She put an arm around Robbie's waist. 'This is wonderful!' she announced, scanning the swirls of orange and red in admiration. 'What is it?'

'A sunset, of course!' Robbie arched his eyebrows in amazement. 'I copied it this morning.'

'Ah, I see!' Cathy smiled at his mistake, thought about

correcting him and then decided against it. 'You are a very clever boy, do you know that?'

'That's what Daniel says.' Robbie's expression was suddenly serious. 'He says I'm not to get cross and upset when the other children tease me at school.'

'They tease you?' Cathy frowned. She stroked back a strand of silky hair from her son's face and looked into his eyes. 'Why? Why do they tease you?'

Robbie looked down at the floor. 'Oh…just because.'

'Because what?' Cathy drew him closer towards her. 'Tell me, darling. Are there some children being horrible to you at school? Is that why you haven't wanted to go all week?'

'I want to go out and play football again!' Robbie struggled away from Cathy's hold.

'But, Robbie—!'

'Let me go!' He was determined. Cathy released her hold and watched in consternation as her son fled from the room.

'Should I go after him, do you think?' she asked, looking worriedly up at Daniel.

'I think he's best left for the moment.'

'You knew about this?' Green eyes narrowed. 'About the bullying, I mean.'

'Not until this morning. I mentioned school when we were painting together. Robbie seemed in the mood to talk.'

'About what?' Cathy couldn't keep the edge from her voice. 'What's been happening?'

'Children can be cruel.' Daniel moved the tray and sat beside Cathy on the window seat. 'They spot a weakness and they use it.'

Cathy frowned. 'A weakness?'

'A *perceived* weakness.' Daniel inhaled a breath and continued. 'It seems a couple of the kids have been playing on the fact that Robbie doesn't have a father.' Cathy closed her eyes briefly. 'Pretty mean, huh?' Daniel's voice was husky with feeling. 'They've come up with some sort of chant.'

She didn't reply. All she could think of in that moment was Steve. His face on that last, dreadful day had been contorted with anger. He had shocked her with the strength of his hatred. How could he have said such cruel things? He had been her first, her *only* boyfriend. Might he have shown more sympathy, actually *wanted* to be a father, if he'd known he had only a few more hours to live?

'Cathy, are you all right?'

She nodded, aware of a great yearning to press herself against the strength of Daniel's body. 'I just feel so...' Cathy shook her head. 'Helpless...alone—'

'You're not alone.' His voice was low and intense. Strong arms drew her in close. Cathy rested her head against his broad chest and closed her eyes. 'I'm here. Robbie will be all right. I'll speak to Miss Stubbs. We can sort this out.'

'Would you?' She twisted her head and looked up at him with glistening eyes. 'I will too, of course,' she added. 'But I'm not sure how much notice she'll take of me.'

She felt like an angel in his arms: more fragile, more needy, more adorable than anyone he had ever known. 'She'll take notice,' Daniel replied grimly; as he was chairman of the school governors, it was a pretty fair bet. 'I'll make sure of it.'

'Thank you.' Cathy lifted her face and kissed him briefly on the mouth.

'What was that for?' he asked huskily.

'For being so...for just being here,' Cathy amended, blushing furiously. 'For caring about Robbie.'

'It's not just Robbie I care about. You surely know that by now?'

'Yes...' Cathy smiled, aware of the vitality in Daniel's gaze, of his expression, his smile, the way his arms felt around her body. I'm such a child, she thought. This is all so new and so wonderful, and yet at the same time frightening, because when have I ever felt like this before?

He lifted a hand and touched her face, stroking a gentle

finger along the line of her jaw. He kissed her mouth. His lips were warm and tender and yet full of the most incredible amount of passion. 'I've wanted to make love to you since the beginning,' he murmured huskily, looking deep into her eyes. 'Ever since that first night in the rain.' He kissed her mouth again, and this time his kiss was a little more demanding, a little more insistent. 'We're going to be good together, Cathy, so good...'

Robbie yelled loudly out in the garden, a gleeful sound, but too noisy to be ignored. Daniel groaned and lifted his head. His mouth curved into a sensuous smile. 'This isn't the time, is it?'

'Maybe not.' They looked at one another, moving apart as if by mutual decision, not touching now, just breathing deeply, gazing into each other's eyes. 'When?' Cathy whispered, conscious of the fear she felt in asking such a question, because to be so open, to risk so much hurt by revealing how much she wanted Daniel, was something she would never imagined possible.

'Tonight...your place.' Daniel's voice was husky with desire. 'I'll bring dinner.'

'Just bring yourself,' Cathy murmured, conscious of the exquisite feeling in the pit of her stomach. 'That will be enough...'

Cathy spent the rest of the morning in a waking dream. She leant against the gnarled trunk of an old apple tree, watching as Daniel chased a squealing Robbie around the garden. He caught him and lifted him high in the air, as had become the routine, then spun him around. Robbie's giggling was infectious. There seemed to be no sign of the anxiety that he had clearly had to deal with over the previous week. Cathy wished she had known sooner, but at least knowing meant she could fix the situation. She would visit the school first thing tomorrow and talk with the formidable Miss Stubbs.

Cathy exhaled a breath. Funny, but she felt stronger, able

to deal with any situation. A surge of happiness over-whelmed her as she gazed at Daniel, holding Robbie high above his head. He was the reason. This breathtakingly handsome, intelligent, humorous man. Everything felt *so* incredible that Cathy wondered seriously for a moment if she hadn't stepped into somebody else's life by mistake.

'Time to chase Mummy!' Daniel lowered Robbie to the floor and took hold of his small hand. 'Better start running, Cathy, or you're going to get caught!' he warned.

Which wouldn't be such a dreadful state of affairs, she thought, as she began to run, dodging this way and that in order to make a proper game of it for Robbie.

'Got you, Mummy!' Robbie grabbed hold of Cathy's leg after all of two minutes and hung on for dear life.

Daniel scooped an arm around her waist. 'Got you!' he whispered against her hair. He turned her towards him. 'There's a forfeit, of course,' he murmured.

'Is there?' Her voice was little more than a whisper.

'Absolutely...' He smiled. 'I enjoyed making love to you so much. Do you believe me?'

Cathy could believe anything in that moment. She stared into Daniel's handsome face in something approaching wonderment.

'Believe it,' he asserted huskily, when she didn't reply, and in the next moment his mouth was covering hers in a deeply passionate kiss.

They walked back to the pub together later that morning, found the Land Rover where they had left it, and journeyed back together to the cottage. 'Thanks so much...' Cathy looked across towards Daniel and smiled shyly '...for ev-erything.'

'It's not over yet, or have you forgotten?' His dark, sen-suous gaze sent a shiver of expectation down Cathy's spine. 'I'd like to stay,' he murmured, 'but I've got some business I need to attend to.' He lightly touched her face with the palm of his hand. 'See you about eight? Until then...' He lowered his head and kissed her softly parted lips. 'Eight,' he repeated huskily.

It wasn't until he'd left the house that Cathy noticed the note, crumpled inside the letterbox...

'Darling, you're looking pleased with yourself. What's happened? Have you sold a painting?'

'Mother, there's no need to make it sound like such a rare occurrence,' Daniel drawled, as he walked into the exquisitely appointed drawing room. 'I do manage to exhibit in Paris and London from time to time.'

'Sorry, darling.' His mother, long stemmed rose in one hand, secateurs in the other, was putting the finishing touches to an impressive floral display. She looked carefully into her son's face. 'So not a painting. Then what?'

'Does it have to be anything?' Daniel picked up a newspaper from a gleaming mahogany side table and glanced at the headlines. He knew only too well how determined his mother could be when she was in this mood—like a dog with the proverbial bone, unable to give up gnawing away until she got to the part she was interested in.

'We haven't seen a great deal of you over the last couple of days. Have you been *very* busy?'

'No busier than usual.' Daniel flipped over and scanned the sports headlines. 'Is Father in his study?'

'Yes, dear, he's been poring over the foundation figures since first thing this morning.' There was a slight pause. 'By the way, someone told me they saw you out walking the other day; you were with a woman and a young boy.'

'Did they?' Daniel kept his eyes focused on the newspaper. 'That's the trouble with this village—too many people are far too preoccupied with other people's business.'

'It was Martha, if you must know. She happened to mention it in passing this morning, when I popped down to the kitchen to talk about the menu for the ball. Incidentally, you do realise this will be the first one you've missed, don't you?'

'That fact has occurred.' Daniel glanced across at his mother and his heart softened a little. She looked incredibly disappointed. He crossed the room and dropped a kiss upon her immaculate grey head. 'You know I have to go to this meeting in London tomorrow, and then I'll be looking around the two new hostels; charity foundations don't run themselves.'

'But if you happen to get back early—?'

Daniel shook his head. 'I'm not promising anything. Besides, you know I dislike the whole rigmarole.'

'Yes, I realise that. But, darling, you've always been there before now. Turning up late would be better than not turning up at all,' she added hopefully.

Daniel released a breath. 'I'll see what I can do.'

'Thank you, sweetheart!' His mother looked radiant suddenly. 'Now this woman—the one you were out walking with—it wasn't the Crawford girl, by any chance, was it? I know she's been showing an interest for some time and at one stage you and she were quite close—'

'It's not her.'

'Or Jane? Evelyn said how smitten she is by you—'

'Not Jane either.' Daniel worked hard at keeping an even tone.

'Well, who was it, then? Martha didn't go into details, although she did say something about an enormous striped jumper.' His mother arched an eyebrow. 'I must say I didn't think that sounded like Jane's style at all—she's always so immaculately turned out...'

Daniel laid the newspaper down and began walking towards the door. 'I'll go and see if Father's ready to discuss the latest figures.'

'But, Daniel, aren't you going to tell me *anything*?'

'No! You'll have to be patient. If I've got anything to tell you, then I'll do it when I'm good and ready and not before.'

Daniel's father was in his study, sitting in front of an impressive walnut desk. He glanced at his son's face. 'Your expression tells me your mother has been giving you the third degree.'

Daniel allowed himself a rueful smile. 'No more than usual.'

'And she wonders why you moved out…' He paused, then cast his son an interested look. 'She seems to think it might be the Crawford girl.'

'Well, it's not.'

'Ah.' His father nodded sagely. 'She's always had a soft spot for Davinia. I told her she was simply believing what she wanted to believe.'

'Once again!' Daniel strolled across towards the window and looked out at the sweeping lawns and impressive parkland. Cathy and Davinia Crawford were as different as chalk and cheese. Davinia was a perfectly pleasant young woman, rather too preoccupied with her appearance, perhaps, but Daniel had never understood why his mother should imagine he would want to spend the rest of his life with her.

He thought of Cathy, of the night just gone, of the one which lay ahead, and felt warmth flood his body. She was the girl he wanted—he knew that with all his heart.

'The gardens are looking good this year,' he commented abruptly. 'Briggs has done a marvellous job. I must tell him when I see him.'

His father smiled. 'Not exactly a subtle change of subject.'

'No.' Daniel's mouth curved. He turned from the window. 'It's honestly a mystery to me why Mother feels she has to keep delving. Surely it's obvious that I'll tell her about any important decisions or changes in my life if and when I make them?'

'Yes, but you know what your mother is like.' His father began sifting through some sheaves of paper. 'If she thinks there's even the remotest chance you've found someone who makes you happy, then she wants to know all the details. Martha seemed to think there was something special between you and this girl she saw you with.'

'Did she?' Daniel looked interested.

'That's what she said.' His father smiled as he gathered up the papers on his desk and slid them into a file, before handing them across to Daniel. 'Can I make one suggestion?'

Daniel raised dark brows. 'Anything.'

'If you have found someone—' His father lifted his hands in a gesture of self-defence. 'And I'm not saying you have. But when you do—and it *will* happen, sooner or later—then can you please make sure your mother is the first to know?' His father's mouth twisted into a smile. 'After yourself and the lady involved, of course!'

Daniel's mouth curved. 'Seems pretty reasonable.'

'Good.' His father gave a satisfied nod. 'Now, to business…'

He wanted the evening to be as perfect as possible. He felt nervous, almost apprehensive. Daniel smiled softly to himself. Funny what love could do; he had never felt this way before, like a schoolboy on a first date…

He walked up the narrow garden path, conscious of the thudding of his heart. The light was on in the downstairs window. He could see Cathy's outline through the thin material. He thought of her determination to get the house together as quickly as possible. She had done a marvellous job with the little she had. That was one of the things he so admired in her, the way she managed to achieve things out of practically nothing. When he thought of the advantages Jane and Davinia and he himself had had…

Daniel knocked at the front door. Mrs Barnet was looking out of her window and he raised a hand in acknowledgement.

Cathy appeared. 'Hello!' Her smile was strained; she sounded a little breathless.

'Hello, yourself!' He leant forward and kissed her mouth. 'You look as wonderful as ever.'

'No, I don't!' She jerked away, dragging a hand through her long auburn hair in a distracted fashion. 'I've been held up...' She shook her head. 'I haven't had a chance to put any make-up on.'

'That black gunge Robbie was talking about?' Daniel's smile was full of good humour. 'Don't worry about it! I happen to find the fresh, unadorned look much more attractive.' He waited a moment, regarding her with a vaguely puzzled expression. 'Aren't you going to invite me in?'

'Yes! Yes, of course!' Cathy stood back so that Daniel could enter the house.

She seemed dazed, a little unsure. 'Is something wrong?' He was becoming genuinely concerned. 'You look a little...frantic.'

'No! No, not at all, it's just—' She shook her head, as if the possibility of explaining was beyond her. She looked up into his face with glistening eyes. 'It's lovely to see you,' she murmured. 'The hours have seemed like days.'

'For me too.' Daniel reached out a hand and touched her face, drawing her close towards him. His kiss was slow and sure and very sensuous.

Finally Cathy said, 'Robbie's in bed. He's tired out, but he's been waiting for you to arrive. Would you mind saying goodnight? He'd really appreciate it.'

'Of course.' Daniel handed Cathy the large carrier bag he was holding. 'I've brought dinner. There's wine and a takeaway—I hope you like Chinese?'

'Yes, wonderful! I haven't had it in ages!' Cathy took the bags from him with a smile which went some way to dispelling his concerns. 'I'll go and get everything ready.'

'Don't do it all!' He caught her arm as she turned away and pulled her to him. She tasted so sweet. Her lips trembled beneath his mouth. He drew back and looked into her face and was more than a little relieved when he saw a soft smile. 'I'll be down in a moment.'

Daniel gently pushed open the door of Robbie's bedroom and glanced toward the bed. For a moment it looked as if he was asleep, surrounded by picture books, clutching a battered teddy under one arm, then Robbie opened one eye and grinned. 'I've been waiting ages!' he announced cheekily.

'Hello, scamp!' Daniel crossed to the bed and picked up the books, which were in danger of sliding onto the floor, and placed them in a pile on the bedside table. 'Everything all right?'

'Sort of.'

Daniel smiled. 'Only sort of?'

'I'm not supposed to say.'

'Say what?' Daniel sat on the edge of the bed. 'Don't tell me you've been in trouble!'

'No, it wasn't me! It's Gary.'

Daniel's brows drew together in a frown. 'Gary?'

'Yes. She thought I didn't know, but I did. Gary was here.'

'Gary…?' Daniel thought for a second. 'You mean the man who helped you to move in?'

'Yes. He's nice sometimes, but I don't like him when he shouts.' Robbie looked fierce suddenly.

Daniel inhaled a steadying breath. 'He was shouting?'

'Not this time, no. But he can.' Robbie narrowed his eyes. 'I've heard him say a naughty word once.'

Daniel looked down at Robbie's concerned expression, his mind reeling with the possibilities of what had taken place. So that was why Cathy had not seemed herself just now. 'Well, don't worry, I'll go downstairs now and talk to Mummy—'

'No, you mustn't do that!' Robbie looked anxious. 'She made me promise not to tell and I've told.' His face showed surprise, almost as if it had happened without him realising it. 'Daniel, please don't! Wait until Mummy tells you, then it will be all right.'

He had a point, Daniel thought, as he descended the stairs a moment later. Perhaps it would be preferable if he allowed Cathy to bring up the subject of Gary's visit herself.

'Is Robbie all right?'

Daniel glanced across at Cathy's anxious expression, then picked up the bottle of wine from the kitchen table and proceeded to pour them both a drink. 'Yes. He's very sleepy.'

'Good.' Cathy looked across at Daniel and wished she could thrust all thoughts of Gary from her mind. She didn't want anything to mar the hours ahead. Damn! Why had he had to call around—tonight of all nights! She had read the note he had hastily thrust through the letterbox with a sinking heart; her instincts had been right. It wasn't about being social. He needed money.

Cathy shook her head. Typical. *So* typical. He was a foolish, foolish boy; she and many others had told him so a thousand times, but it didn't seem to make any difference. Cathy wondered what the attraction of those machines was. After all, everybody knew the odds were stacked against, so why did he keep on gambling—throwing his money away?

He had practically begged that she help him. She knew he was doing the rounds—a bit here, a bit there—and he had taken the little she had given him with barely a word of thanks. It had not been nice, seeing him in such a state, and she had had to be strong; if he had even guessed that she had been saving a little each week for Robbie's birthday, then…well, she didn't like to dwell on the consequences. Desperation was a horrible thing; it could make you do things you usually wouldn't dream of…

'You look tense.'

'Do I?' Cathy glanced away. 'I suppose it's because I'm not used to this sort of thing.'

Daniel raised an eyebrow. '"This sort of thing"?' he queried. 'You mean us...this evening?'

'Everything!' The word was expelled on a breath. 'I don't think you understand how amazing all this is for me—how amazing you are,' she added softly. 'One minute I'm living in the middle of a run-down inner-city estate feeling indescribably lonely, the next—'

'You felt *that* bad?' Daniel frowned. His jaw tightened. 'I wish I could have been there for you—'

'You're here now,' Cathy replied. 'That's the important thing.' She hesitated, but only for a moment. 'I had a visit earlier—from Gary, the guy who helped me move in.'

'I know.'

'How do you—? Robbie!' Cathy murmured.

'Robbie,' Daniel agreed. 'He seemed worried for you.'

'Did he?' She shook her head. 'He's so young, yet so grown-up in many ways.'

'Do you want to tell me what it was all about?'

'There's nothing to tell. It was just a...social call.' Cathy avoided Daniel's gaze and asked forgiveness for such a blatant lie.

'You were tense and unhappy when I arrived—that had nothing to do with him?' he asked quietly.

'His visit threw me a little, that's all.' Cathy noticed Daniel hadn't touched his food. 'I was looking forward to seeing you so much...'

Daniel decided not to put any more pressure on her. '*So much?*' There was a twinkle in his eyes suddenly. He pulled her close. 'How much?' he asked huskily. 'As much as this?'

His mouth was warm and tender. Cathy closed her eyes and allowed herself the luxury of thinking only of the moment, only of Daniel and how much he meant to her.

He scooped her into his arms. Neither of them spoke; it wasn't a time for words. Cathy longed to be possessed by him. To feel wanted like this was the most miraculous thing—to want someone so much...

It was more than just desire. She knew that. She loved him. Every action, every look. The way he spoke, the things he said—all of it. He was everything she had ever dreamed about: handsome, kind, selfless, humorous. Daniel turned his head and saw her watching him. 'I want you,' he told her huskily, looking deep into her eyes. 'More than I've ever wanted anyone else…'

He felt happy. So tremendously happy. All the pieces of the jigsaw had fallen into place at last. This was it. This was what he had been waiting for—*who* he had been waiting for. Except, of course, he hadn't known—not until now…

Daniel propped himself up on one elbow and looked at Cathy lying beside him. She was asleep. He touched her hair, lifting a silky strand away from her face. He looked into her face, studying every inch, marvelling at the strength of feeling which totally consumed him. This was the woman he wanted to spend the rest of his life with. He loved her.

He thought of the day which lay ahead; a trip to London didn't appeal—not at all—but there was no way he could cancel at such a late stage. Had he even told her about his trip to London? He wasn't sure. Travel arrangements had been the last thing on his mind last night, or the night before come to that…

Daniel glanced at his wristwatch and saw to his dismay that he really needed to be up and on his way if he was to catch the early train. Should he wake her and tell her? Instinct told him to leave her sleeping. Damn! He didn't want to go away, even if it was only for two days and a night. He thought of the responsibilities he held now that his father had made him head of the foundation; so many people were relying on him. He couldn't ignore them— didn't *want* to ignore them.

What to do, then? He looked at Cathy again and considered asking her to come with him, even though he knew that that was an impractical solution; there was no time, and besides, there was Robbie to consider.

Daniel's gaze fell upon the third finger of Cathy's left hand and a shock of inspiration fell upon him. It felt absolutely right. A culmination of all his hopes and desires. But how would Cathy react if he returned from London with a ring and got down on bended knee?

'Sweet darling...' His voice was husky with feeling. He watched as the woman he loved stirred faintly, stretching languorous arms above her head. Daniel lowered his head and kissed the soft pale skin at the base of her throat. The temptation to continue their lovemaking was strong—stronger than he had ever known in his life before. But now that his trip to London had another purpose, he found it easier to fight against the desire which gripped his body.

Daniel gazed lovingly down into Cathy's face. There had been wonderment in her eyes, a look of love coupled with joy and amazement which had made his heart soar way, way up into the night sky.

This was it. He knew he had found the woman he wanted to spend the rest of his life with. Daniel lifted the corner of the duvet and slid his naked body out of bed. Muscles rippled in the morning light as he pulled on trousers and shirt. He turned and looked down at Cathy's sleeping face.

'Soon,' he murmured softly, glancing around the dismal room, 'all this will change. I promise you.'

CHAPTER EIGHT

'MUMMY. It's very messy in the living room.'

Cathy raised her head distractedly. 'Is it?'

'I found your blouse.' Robbie bounced onto the bed and handed it to her. 'What's that?'

'A note from Daniel.'

'Why?'

'He's had to go to London—to a meeting. He'll be back on Friday.'

'What does it say?'

Cathy scanned the contents of the note for the twentieth time and gave Robbie a short, censored resumé. 'Well...Daniel says that he's going to miss us, and that he had a very nice time last night...' Cathy paused. 'A very nice time,' she repeated softly, re-reading his words. 'And that he can't wait until he comes back to see us again.' Cathy folded up the note and put it in the drawer of the bedside cabinet. 'So we're just going to have to be patient, aren't we? Two days isn't so long.'

She knew she was trying to convince herself. Waking up and finding him gone had been awful. Even seeing the note placed carefully on the pillow beside her had sent dread and anxiety rushing through her body. He would come back, wouldn't he? After last night... She inhaled a deep, steadying breath. She could still scarcely believe how much Daniel had wanted her—but he had, he *had*! There was no mistaking the depth of his desire; every touch, every kiss had been full of passionate intensity. He had been so...*magnificent*, showing her tenderness and passion in a way that she had only ever dreamed about. She just wished he were here now, to show her all over again. She needed reassurance. If it had just been easy words and empty gestures, then she didn't know what she would do, or how she would cope...

'Hey! Look at the time!' Cathy threw back the bedcovers. 'You're going to be late for school.'

'Don't want to go!' Robbie stuck his bottom lip out in a defiant manner. 'Don't want to!'

'Oh, sweetheart...' Cathy cuddled him close. 'I know you don't want to go now, but remember what Daniel said to you yesterday? You have to be brave and strong.'

'Like him?' Robbie queried.

'Yes,' Cathy replied, hugging her son close. 'Just like him...'

'Well, here's someone who looks as if they're having a good day!' Cathy closed the door of the village store behind her and picked up a shopping basket. She had just dropped Robbie off at school and there had been no clinging or crying or difficulty of any sort. She had even taken Miss Stubbs to task about the bullying, and had been pleased to hear her assertion that she would deal with it. Cathy smiled at the woman behind the counter. 'You must be pleased,' the woman continued. 'So new to the village. It's an ideal opportunity to meet folks.'

Cathy frowned. 'Sorry? I don't know...'

'Haven't you seen the list in the window? You're one of the lucky winners.'

'I am?' Cathy struggled to marshal her thoughts. They were all over the place this morning—no, that wasn't true; they were just elsewhere. She had felt as if she had entered fantasy land last night, and even now, going over and over each and every incredible moment, she still found it hard to believe that everything had been real. 'What have I won?'

The woman behind the counter smiled indulgently. 'Tickets to the ball! There are posters all around the village. It's tomorrow night.'

'Oh…!' Cathy shook her head slightly, smiling in amazement. 'I had no idea.'

'The winning list has been up since the middle of last week,' the woman replied, almost disapprovingly. 'Everyone else has called by.'

'Oh…well, I'm here now,' Cathy responded brightly. Then her face fell. 'But really there's no point in me having them.' She pictured her wardrobe of clothes. 'You have to dress up, don't you? And I've got nothing to wear, nor anyone to go with.'

'Oh, we don't let little things like that make any difference!' The woman lifted the old-fashioned wooden counter. 'Lots of people go on their own, and as for a suitable outfit…' Her watery blue eyes twinkled. 'Come on upstairs with me.'

'Upstairs?' Cathy repeated, glancing uncertainly through to the back of the shop.

'You're new to the village—I'm forgetting.' The old woman smiled. 'I run a bit of a hire shop: fancy dress, glamorous costumes and the like. It's a good little business. I'm the only one in the area and you'd be surprised how often people are needing one or the other. Of course my busiest time is Christmas, what with all the parties and that, but the spring ball at the manor house always boosts my trade. Anyway, you come up with me and see if anything takes your fancy—of course a lot of the best stuff has gone, but there are one or two dresses left which might fit the bill…'

'Here we are!'

Cathy climbed the last stair in something of a daze and stood beside the woman. The clothes were stored in a room above the shop. Everything was very neat and professional-looking. At the far end of the room Cathy could see several rails holding fancy dress costumes: cowboy and sailor suits, feathered hats, all manner of weird and wonderful creations. Closer to hand were the traditional ballgowns. Cathy spied layers of tangerine net and a ghastly dress in gold lamé amongst the offerings, and gave a mental shudder.

'As you can see, the rails are pretty depleted,' the old woman commented, walking towards them. She flicked through briskly, thankfully not pausing at the more extrovert creations. 'But, as I said, there might still be something which takes your fancy.' She glanced over to where Cathy stood and smiled encouragingly. 'Come on, dear, take a look.'

Cathy strolled over to the rails. She still wasn't sure if she even wanted to go to the ball. On her own? It wasn't her scene—she had never been to a ball in her life before, and after the debacle at Sandra's house at the weekend, her confidence wasn't exactly sky-high...

'I'm not sure I even want to go,' Cathy murmured.

'Not go?' The old woman sounded shocked. *'Not go?'* she repeated, looking at Cathy as if she were mad. 'But you've won the tickets, and it's such a good evening! Practically the whole village turns out, and there's wonderful food and music and lots of dancing!' She pulled a dress off the rail and held it up. 'What about this?'

Cathy eyed the red and black lace garment with misgivings. It was too low at the neck and it had a large swirling skirt. She'd end up looking like a Spanish dancer.

'I don't think it's me.'

'This one?' Pale green this time, with an extravagant design of sequins.

'To tell you the truth,' Cathy murmured, 'I can't really afford to hire anything.'

'Oh, my rates are very reasonable.'

'Even so...'

The old woman cast sympathetic eyes over Cathy's well-worn outfit. 'Well...' She thought for a moment. 'As the ball's tomorrow night, and most people have already got their outfits organised, I think I could stretch to a special rate. I'd rather see the dresses being used than sitting here on the hangers.'

'What sort of special rate?' Cathy asked, visualising the contents of her purse. 'Only, I need to get some groceries and—'

The old woman mentioned a figure. It was extremely reasonable—bordering, if Cathy were honest, on charity. 'That's very kind of you.' She smiled warmly, trying to decide what to do. 'Are you sure that's OK?'

'Yes, of course, dear.' The shop bell rang downstairs. 'Now you just take your time and see what you can find. I've got to go and serve a customer.'

Cathy considered the prospect of attending the ball more seriously. Well, why not? It would certainly be one way to fill the hours before Daniel returned. Now that the idea had taken hold, she found herself feeling quite excited at the prospect, but only, she thought, looking at the rails of clothes, if she could find something suitable to wear.

Cathy riffled through the racks.

She paused at a limp-looking dress in chocolate-brown. It was demure and understated, and without sequins or glitter or lace or anything else which might make her stand out from the crowd. Cathy held it up and considered it dispassionately. She could understand why it had been passed by; it didn't look like very much at all. She glanced around the room and saw a small changing cubicle in the corner. She drew the flowery curtain across, slipped off her jeans and jumper and pulled the dress on over her head.

Cathy stared at her reflection in amazement. Who would have thought it? Her bra wasn't right, because the dress was halter-necked, but that didn't matter because everything else was…well, it was almost perfect. Her mouth curved into an astonished smile. She looked better than she would ever have imagined. There was something about the colour of the dress which brought out the best both in her hair and her complexion, and the fit was not bad at all—a little slack around the bust, maybe, but that could easily be fixed with a few careful stitches. Cathy made her decision. She *would* go.

'How did you get on, dear?' The shopkeeper asked as Cathy came back downstairs. 'Anything take your fancy, did it?'

'Yes, actually it did.' Cathy smiled brightly, laying the dress onto the counter so that the old woman could see it. 'I'd like this one.'

At least the prospect of attending the ball had the advantage of keeping Cathy's thoughts from continually dwelling on Daniel. No contact for two whole days, particularly after sharing such intense intimacy, was proving to be extremely difficult to handle. She wondered where he was, what he was doing, whether he still cared, at least fifty times a day. If only she'd had a phone at the cottage. He had left a number on the note he had left for her, but when she had walked to the local phone box with Robbie after school yesterday the number had been unattainable. She had tried not to let it worry her, manufacturing a million reasons why it might be so, and whenever the doubts became too strong she would rush upstairs to her bedside cabinet and re-read his note.

'So, what do you think of this then, Robbie? Better than last time?'

'Much better!' Robbie appraised the brown frock with a serious eye. 'You look like a posh person on the television.'

'Do I?' Cathy regarded herself in the mirror. There was no doubt the dress did something for her—no doubt at all. She looked positively sophisticated, which was just as well, given the grand location of the ball, she thought.

'Now, Mrs Barnet will read a story to you downstairs and then you are to go straight to bed,' Cathy instructed. 'No nonsense or naughtiness!' She bent down and lifted her son into her arms and kissed him tenderly. 'I won't be late, sweetheart.'

It took some nerve, walking down the lane to the large house on her own, but Cathy was determined to do it. New experiences made life more interesting, she told herself firmly, as she carefully picked her way along the edges of the verge. She held her torch clearly so that the passing cars—and there were any number of them travelling towards the manor house—would be sure to see her and give her a reasonably wide berth.

The house looked magnificent. Every window was lit up and there were fairy lights strung between the trees of the drive. As Cathy entered the grounds the sound of music floated up magically into the night air.

She took a deep breath as she entered the grand hallway. Now that she was actually here she felt distinctly unsure of herself, and quite, quite alone. Maybe this wasn't such a good idea. Cathy looked around at the clusters of people all talking excitedly amongst themselves. No one would be any the wiser if she turned around now and headed back home…

'Well, I wish I could say I'm surprised to see you here!' Sandra's somewhat caustic voice sliced through the noise of fifty conversations. She was dressed in midnight-blue and looked stunning, as usual. 'Where's Daniel?' Her blue eyes flitted around impatiently. 'I didn't think he was supposed to be here.'

'He's not. He's in London.' Cathy smoothed down the silky fabric of her dress which, she discovered, had a tendency to cling.

'From the village store is it?' Sandra's gaze was disparaging. 'Not as bad as some of the outfits here this evening, but it's got 'hire me' written all over it. London, you say? His charity work, I suppose?'

Cathy nodded, determined not to allow Sandra's attitude to get the better of her. 'Are you here with someone?' she enquired in neutral tones.

'Yes.' Sandra's reply was short. 'He's just parking the car.' She glanced around at the milling throng, eyeing up everybody who came near. 'Some people just have no taste!' she murmured, as a woman in a particularly gaudy pink and orange outfit passed by. 'So, is Daniel going to put in an appearance later?'

Cathy shook her head. 'No, I told you; he's in London.'

'Bit of a let-down for you, I should think,' Sandra commented, 'him not being here.' Her mouth curved, and Cathy could see the effort needed to maintain a semblance of affability. 'You know, I never would have believed it, not in a million years! When I spied you at his house that day...' A mixture of expressions collided across her face. 'You and he have got very cosy in such a short space of time, haven't you?'

'Cosy?' Cathy wasn't sure about that particular description. 'We've become close,' she murmured, after a moment.

'Of course, that's the only thing about Daniel,' Sandra replied acidly. 'He always feels he's got to do things differently. I suppose it's his way of rebelling.'

Cathy frowned, not sure what Sandra was getting at. 'Look, I realise you must be finding this a little difficult to deal with, but—'

'I hope you're making the most of this.' Sandra gestured towards their grand surroundings. 'Because it will be over before you can blink.' She paused, her fixed smile belying the offensive nature of her words. 'I know Daniel's type: the novelty of a situation attracts him initially, and then, when that wears off, he'll move on and upwards to better things.'

'Is that so?' Cathy replied coolly. She found, to her own amazement, that she really couldn't be bothered to get angry. Sandra was beside herself with jealousy about her relationship with Daniel; it was a simple as that. 'Well, you'll have to excuse me, but I came here to enjoy myself, not to listen to the rantings of an envious woman.' Cathy smiled sweetly. 'Have a nice evening, Sandra!'

She moved off, releasing a huge sigh of relief when she

was a safe distance from Sandra's vehement gaze. She was shaking like a leaf, but felt proud of the way she had handled that; it would have been all too easy to allow Sandra's horrible words to upset her.

Cathy ventured nervously into the ballroom. It seemed as if the whole of the village was in attendance. The string quartet were playing a feet-tapping waltz and already several couples were whirling around the floor, seemingly determined to make the most of the evening's entertainment.

Cathy picked up a glass from a passing tray and looked about her. Everything was *so* grand. It was like a scene from a film: glittering chandeliers, classical music, waiting staff dressed neatly in black and white weaving their way carefully amongst the guests with silver trays held expertly at shoulder height.

She wished Daniel were here to join in the fun—for it could be fun. Cathy smiled as she watched a young couple gaily throwing themselves into the dancing.

'Fancy a try?'

Cathy turned. It was one of the guests from the disastrous evening at Sandra's. She racked her brain, trying to think of his name.

'Colin.' He held out his hand. 'Not wearing feathers this evening, then?'

Cathy blushed, then laughed. 'No,' she admitted, 'I thought I'd steer well clear...'

Once the ice was broken Cathy soon found herself enjoying any number of invitations to dance, and accepted each one with alacrity.

After hours of virtually non-stop dancing, she found herself feeling hot, tired and extremely hungry. A long gallery linked the ballroom with the room where the buffet was laid. Cathy walked slowly along, regarding the portraits lining the panelled walls with interest: several generations of the Hamilton men, and every one of them looked distinguished. She tried to imagine what it must be like to live in such a place as this, and found it too much of a jump for her imagination...

Daniel tossed his bag onto a nearby chair and headed for the kitchen. He needed food. There had been a fault with the train just outside Reading, which had meant a frustrating wait in a siding for nearly ninety minutes before being transferred to another train which didn't have a buffet car.

The phone rang. Daniel pulled out some ham and a slab of butter from the refrigerator and lifted the receiver. 'Yes?'

'Daniel, is that you? Darling, you're back! Why aren't you here?'

'Hello, Mother.' He tucked the handset beneath his chin and proceeded to butter bread. 'Look, I've just this minute walked through the door—'

'But you are coming over?'

He inhaled a breath, put down the butter knife and glanced at his wristwatch. It was nearly eleven-thirty. Damn that train! 'Do you really want me there?'

'Oh, darling, you know how much it means to me. Please! I know you think I'm making a fuss about nothing, but it's not the same without you. Lots of people have asked where you are.'

Daniel gave it a moment's thought. It would be selfish to go round to Cathy's now and wake her up anyway, however much he wanted to. First thing in the morning would do just as well for what he had planned. Daniel felt for the box in his jacket pocket. He must put the ring in his safe before he left. 'OK, I'll be over as soon as I can.'

'You'll wear your dinner jacket?'

'If it means that much to you, Mother, then, yes, I'll wear my dinner jacket,' Daniel replied wearily.

Cathy had returned from the buffet with a satisfying selection of food. It had been worth the wait. The service might have been on the slow side, but the quality or the quantity of the food hadn't deteriorated in the least.

The main hall was very full and hot now. Cathy squeezed around the edges of the room, careful to avoid the dancing couples.

'I thought you said he wasn't going to be able to make it tonight? What's the matter—have the two of you had a tiff?'

Cathy frowned at Sandra. She didn't need this right now. All she wanted to do was to find a quiet corner so that she could sit down and eat some food in peace. 'I don't know what you're talking about,' she murmured.

'Have you been a little economical with the truth? Don't tell me I've jumped to the wrong conclusion? Yes!' Sandra's smile was bordering on the triumphant. 'Silly me! I thought it was rather a fantastical state of affairs.' She shook her blonde head sagely. 'I mean, the idea of you two together—it's ridiculous!'

'Sandra, will you please go away? I'm not in the mood for your riddles.'

'You and Daniel aren't together at all, are you?' Sandra continued, glancing across to the other side of the ballroom with a satisfied smile. 'It was just a simple one-night stand.'

'Sandra, I think you ought to be quiet!' Cathy shook her head in amazement, conscious of the close proximity of the other guests. 'My private life has absolutely *nothing* to do with you!' she hissed, glancing around her. 'Now, will you just keep—?'

He was here! Cathy stared in amazement at the vision of Daniel, dressed in an immaculate dinner jacket, standing across the other side of the room chatting to the host and hostess. *He was here.* Her heart soared. She could scarcely believe it. How could it be? Why…? The breath caught in her throat as she struggled to find some explanation for Daniel's sudden appearance.

'He really does look gorgeous, doesn't he?' Sandra murmured. 'Well, I can't deny I envy you. One night with him is surely better than no night at all...'

Cathy hardly heard what Sandra was saying. It was hot and stuffy and she wasn't sure what was going on. She watched as Daniel glanced towards the whirling couples, surveying the scene with an almost disinterested eye. He looked... Cathy swallowed, conscious of the heat which was rushing through her body...different. Not like the man she knew. Not at all...

'Of course, he's known to be a ladies' man—you can't say I didn't warn you about that,' Sandra continued. 'And he's heavily involved in his family's charitable foundation. I just never imagined he'd link the two together...' She looked pointedly at Cathy. 'His mother looks a lot happier now, doesn't she? In some ways it's a pity Daniel didn't ask you to attend the ball with him; it would have been worth it just to see her expression—she's very conscious of class and station and all that.' Sandra watched Cathy's face closely for a reaction. 'Did he ever tell her about the two of you, do you know? No, I don't suppose he did,' she continued. 'Have you spoken to him at all? Or has your relationship disintegrated beyond the level of polite conversation?'

'Be quiet.' Cathy's voice was a ragged whisper. 'Be quiet...' she repeated, gritting her teeth as the consequence of what Sandra was saying began to sink in.

Was Daniel really connected with all this? Cathy looked around her in a daze. It was stuffy and hot and everybody was too close—far too close. A claustrophobic reaction began to well up inside her. She wanted to run, to escape from all this noise and gaiety. She needed a quiet moment to think, to assimilate this new, outrageous piece of information...

At first he didn't trust his own eyes. Love was a powerful emotion—that he could hallucinate, actually imagine that she was here, amongst the crowd...

Daniel looked again, his mouth curving a little in amazement. She *was* here! That was Cathy. But how—why? He focused more closely, still unable to believe his own eyes. She looked…dazed, unhappy. Hell! Had he gone completely mad? She didn't know yet, didn't understand about any of this. He looked around the ballroom, cursing his own foolishness. *Damn!* He should have told her before he left. Damn! Damn…!

'Daniel!' His mother's voice was tinged with surprise. 'Where are you going?'

'Not now, Mother!'

The room was ridiculously crowded and he was having difficulty getting to her. The music came to an end and the couples on the dance floor gathered around the slightly elevated platform on which his father stood, making the crush even worse. He had always disliked this part of the evening, when everyone gathered into the main hall to hear his father's friendly but highly predictable speech about the importance of village life and the pleasure it always gave him to host the spring ball and subsequent festivities.

Daniel searched for Cathy. He felt anxiety scorch through his body. She seemed to have disappeared. Hell! He should never have allowed this to happen. To go away without making sure she knew the complete truth…

Then he saw her. She looked different now. Her eyes were wide and glassy, and she looked pale. Daniel skirted round a tightly gathered group, pushed through another, unaware of the curious glances he was receiving…

She fled before he could reach her. There was no way in the world she could simply stand still and wait for him to come to her. Cathy retraced her steps along the gallery. Her only thought was to get away from the crowds, to get away from Daniel. Cathy glanced up at the portraits of the Hamilton men as she ran past. Their eyes seemed to follow her frantic path; there was almost mockery in their gaze. *Daniel was one of them!* Had he been mocking her too, with his generous compliments and easy charm?

She had no idea where she was headed. Cathy swerved away from the buffet area and ran along a narrower corridor. There were several doors on either side. She halted at one, and without stopping to think grabbed the handle and fled inside...

'Who is she?'

'A friend.'

'Did you know she was going to be here tonight?'

'No.' Daniel shook his head. 'No, I didn't.' He pulled his bow tie apart and undid the top button of his dress shirt. 'Are you sure you haven't seen her?'

'Does she live in the village?'

'Yes.' Daniel inhaled a steadying breath and let it out slowly. He tried to keep a calm façade, but it wasn't easy. 'She moved in a couple of weeks ago.'

'You're...' his father hesitated '...close?'

Daniel paused and stopped scanning the assembled guests from his vantage point high up on the gallery which encompaased three sides of the ballroom. He met his father's gaze. 'Yes,' he replied. 'We're close.'

'Ahh!' His father nodded his grey head once or twice. 'I see. Well, I'll go back downstairs and explain to your mother. She was quite taken aback at your rushed departure from the ballroom.'

'She's here somewhere.' Daniel's dark eyes surveyed the throng below. 'I asked Carter whether he had seen anyone pass him as soon as she left the ballroom, but no one's left the house—at least not by the front entrance.'

'All the rear entrances are locked, to prevent uninvited guests.' His father looked at Daniel for a moment. 'Why would your...friend want to leave anyway? Or is that too much of a loaded question?'

Daniel shook his head. 'I can't explain now, Father. Perhaps later...' He turned and began descending the stairs of the gallery. 'I must find her...talk to her...explain...'

*   *   *

Cathy paced back and fro. She glanced down at her feet; if she wasn't careful she'd wear out what looked like an extremely expensive carpet... Tears spilled from her lashes and dripped down her cheeks. She couldn't leave the room until she had got a grip of herself, but that was proving to be easier said than done. How could he do this to her? *How?* All her hopes, her dreams, dashed in a moment. Cathy relived the moment when everything had fallen into place. I was mad, she told herself, to imagine that someone like Daniel... He was far too wonderful to ever be a possibility for someone like me. She gulped a tearful breath. This is real life, not fantasy land. Dreams don't come true— at least not the sort of dreams I've been thinking about...

She thought about the times he had visited the cottage. No wonder he had looked aghast at the damp wallpaper and rotten window frames! It must have been pity. Cathy's jaw tightened. Yes, pity and lust. Just about the most horrible combination she could think of—

The door opened and Cathy froze, staring at the ever widening space with a tormented expression of anger and misery.

'*Cathy!*' The relief on Daniel's face was clearly evident. He entered the room looking lethally impressive in his dinner jacket. Cathy noticed the bow tie at his neck was hanging loose, that a few strands of his silky dark hair were out of place—clearly her unexpected appearance had had its effect. He closed the door behind him. 'Sweetheart, I've been looking for you everywhere—'

'Don't!' Cathy held up her hand as Daniel came towards her. 'Don't come near me!'

He frowned. 'But we need to talk!'

'Do we?' Cathy's expression was hard. She looked up into Daniel's handsome face for a moment, before wide, green eyes swept the room. They were in a bedroom: large and ornate, with wooden panelling and lots of rich silk drapes and tapestries. 'Funny, but I'm not in the mood for conversation.'

'Cathy, are you all right?' She heard the consternation in his voice, saw the worried expression. 'Do you want me to call a doctor? You look pale.' He was frowning. Cathy looked into his dark eyes and thought about all the lies.

'What do you expect?' Her voice was like a razor: sharp, cutting. *This isn't me,* she thought to herself. *I don't want to sound like this, to feel like this…* 'I don't need a doctor, Daniel,' she announced firmly. She looked into his face and her gaze was bleak. 'I just need to go home.'

CHAPTER NINE

'CATHY, give me a chance—!'

'I want to go home.'

'Not yet.' Daniel moved and blocked Cathy's path to the door. 'Let me explain.'

'I don't want your explanations.' Cathy's voice was hard. She looked up and saw the shock in Daniel's eyes. Maybe no one had spoken to him like this before, she thought. Maybe all the girls he had ever made love to simpered sweetly and did whatever he asked. 'I just want to go home,' she repeated.

'Cathy...!' He shook his head a little, placed a hand on her arm. 'I never meant to deceive you.'

'But you did.' Her voice was flat. Funny, she thought, how easily she could banish the emotion from her voice when it really mattered. A defence mechanism, she supposed, designed to prevent as much hurt and humiliation as possible.

'Cathy—!'

'Will you let go of me?'

He hesitated a moment, looking at her, assessing, perhaps, the strength of her dislike. 'It doesn't have to be this way,' he murmured roughly, lifting his hands from her body.

'Oh, but I think it does,' Cathy replied swiftly. She looked around the bedroom; it was practically large enough to engulf the whole of her small house. She imagined what he must have thought when he'd entered her place for the very first time, and then the time after that, and the one after that... 'I'm not interested in men who lie and deceive,' she said. 'I've had enough of that to last me a lifetime!'

'I never meant to deceive—'

'So you keep saying!' Cathy replied harshly. 'What happened?' She gestured with her hands. 'Did all this just slip your mind?'

'I didn't want it to…complicate things.'

Cathy's face twisted into a hard, knowing expression. She thought about Sandra's words earlier that evening and said, 'No. I can imagine. Now…' Cathy looked across at Daniel, but only briefly. She found it far too painful. He did look *so* wealthy, dressed as he was in his dark dinner jacket, with his bow tie hanging casually undone around his tanned neck. 'Will you allow me to go home?'

'You're overreacting.' Daniel's voice was calm. 'Cathy, there's no need to be like this. Nothing's changed. I still feel the same way about you—'

'Bored little rich kid having some fun, do you mean?' Cathy gritted. She shook her head. 'I'm not interested, Daniel. You may still feel the same way, but I don't.'

'You don't mean that—'

'I do.' Her voice shook slightly, but she persevered, determined to finish this thing here and now, to preserve some pride. She looked him in the eyes again. 'Oh, yes!'

He didn't move. He looked dark and dangerous and forbidding. She could feel the tension in his broad frame, see the anger in his eyes. After a moment he said, 'If that's what you want.'

'It is.'

So hard. How could she do it? Years of practice, that was how. Years of putting up a barrier to save her from getting hurt. Years of appearing tough when need be, so that others wouldn't take advantage.

'You must believe that I had no idea you were going to be here tonight.'

Cathy's mouth twisted into a bitter smile. 'And that's supposed to make me feel better, is it?'

'Do you imagine I wanted you to find out this way?'

'It doesn't matter, does it? Because I *have* found out and I *do* know.' Cathy twisted away, biting down on her bottom lip to prevent herself from crying. She clutched at the chocolate-coloured dress she was wearing and twisted the hired fabric through her fingers.

'Cathy...sweetheart, for goodness' sake—!'

'Don't call me that!' She stared, eyes glassy with tears, at a painting of a horse on the wall opposite her. She couldn't cope with much more of this; his words of endearment, however shallow, would make her crack eventually. 'I don't want you to speak to me any more. You've spoilt it—spoilt everything!'

Music floated into the room from the ballroom: a romantic waltz. Cathy thought of how it could have been. In her dreams Daniel would have picked her up and taken her to the ball himself. He would have introduced her to his parents and spent the entire evening dancing with her. They would have sipped champagne on the terrace and he would have found some romantic spot away from the crowds where he would have declared his undying love. In her dreams...

'Cathy, this is madness!'

She heaved a steadying breath. 'Your parents are Lord and Lady Hamilton, aren't they?'

'Yes.' Daniel sounded distracted. 'But that has nothing to do with—'

'That means that one day you'll be a lord or something...' She felt terrible. If she didn't get away soon, she'd break down in tears and make a complete fool of herself. She affected a cultured voice. 'How frightfully exciting!'

'There's no need to be like this!' Now Daniel sounded angry. That was good, wasn't it? What she wanted? He looked at her, and when he spoke his voice was hard and steely. 'You're not helping things.'

'Why the hell should I?' Now she had really blown it— any pretence at cool and control had totally flown out of the window. 'Tell me that! Tell me why on earth I should make things easy for *you*!'

She saw that he wasn't going to beg. He still had his pride. Not that begging would produce the desired result. She wasn't interested in anything he had to say—not right now anyway. Cathy's bottom lip quivered. That expression! So hard and cold. He looked like a different person.

'I'm taking you home.' She didn't argue. 'Did you have a coat?'

'Yes.' Cathy heaved a steadying breath. 'Black, tatty— you know the one,' she continued dryly. 'It went rather well with the purple silk dress the other evening.'

The drive home was almost unbearable. Cathy gave silent thanks that it took only a few minutes for Daniel to manoeuvre the luxurious car along the lanes towards her house. Neither of them spoke—what was there to say? She knew, in her not so infinite wisdom, that she had cancelled out any explanations that Daniel might have wanted to give, prevented any other outcome other than the one where she was miserable and alone once again.

Cathy glanced across briefly as Daniel brought the car to a halt outside her house. He looked tired; his expression was strained. It was like looking into a mirror. For one desperate moment she felt the compulsion to throw herself into his arms, to bury her head against his chest and pretend that everything was normal again—that they were just two normal people with every possibility of a future together.

'Goodnight.'

'Goodnight, Cathy.' His voice was gravelly. This wasn't how things were supposed to be—not at all. He had never imagined she could look so cold and hostile. He thought of the solitaire diamond ring he had bought in London, of the beautiful evening dress which had caught his eye in an exclusive shop window... Had he really got it so wrong? He glanced across at Cathy's face and knew that he had.

He felt stunned, almost unable to think coherently in the face of such animosity. 'I'll phone you.'

'I haven't got a phone—remember? Incidentally, were those numbers you wrote on that note just a string of unconnected digits—or did you really want me to phone you whilst you were away?'

'You couldn't get through?'

Cathy's mouth twisted into a painful smile. 'You sound surprised.'

'Cathy—for goodness' sake! Why are you being so damned difficult about this?'

'*Difficult?*' Cathy could hardly believe her ears. 'What did you expect?'

'I'm going to call by tomorrow, talk to you—' Daniel began.

'No!' Her voice was like a knife. 'No,' she repeated, a little less stridently. 'Don't do that.'

'*What?* Are you serious?' Anger and amazement filled the car. 'We can't just leave it like this!'

'I think it's for the best.' Cathy removed her seat belt and began to open the door. Her voice was clipped, cold. 'There's no future for us, Daniel, surely you see that?'

'We've slept together, for God's sake! Doesn't that *mean* anything to you?' Anger ripped through Daniel's body. He reached across and slammed the door shut. 'OK, so I took my time telling you about my money—!'

'You lied!' Cathy turned towards him, her face on fire. 'You lied!' she repeated. 'Doesn't *that* mean anything to you! How did you think I felt, seeing you this evening? I had no idea—no idea at all! And you expect me to just be the sweet, downtrodden little woman and take it!'

'Downtrodden?' Daniel's brow creased into a furrow. 'Where the hell did you get that word from? What has "downtrodden" got to do with it? There was a misunderstanding—'

'A *misunderstanding?*' Cathy's temper rose. 'You lied!

You deceived me! I never want to see your face again. Do you hear me? Do you? Do you—!'

His mouth had descended before she had a chance to repeat it one more time. He had got the message, but that didn't prevent him from wanting her, still loving her. His kiss was a torturous mix of punishment and pleasure. He wasn't thinking straight any more—not that he had ever done so; not since the first moment he'd set eyes on her. She affected his whole being, body and soul. He wanted her so much it was untrue. He held her close against his muscular frame, his mouth forcing her lips apart, his tongue searching and exploring the moist contours of her mouth. He felt her body weaken, and for a moment it was enough to continue, to forget the words and explanations and simply show her how much he wanted her.

Then realisation dawned. *What on earth was he doing?* He thrust her from him, realising, but only when it was too late, that he was behaving like some sort of deranged and desperate fool. How had that made things better? Daniel cursed silently. One look at Cathy's expression told him it had only made things worse.

'I'm sorry.' His voice was devoid of emotion. 'I didn't mean that to happen.' His thoughts rushed across the wasteland that had been the evening, and his jaw clenched as he strove for composure.

'I've got to go.' Cathy wrenched open the passenger door and got out.

'I'll walk you to your door.'

'No!'

He saw the strain on her face and decided not to push it. Daniel watched carefully as Cathy walked to her front door. Once she was safely inside, he thrust the car into gear and roared away.

Cathy slipped off her coat and hung it on the peg in the hallway. Gary appeared. 'All right? Thought I heard voices.' He glanced briefly at Cathy, 'Nice motor. Always fancied a Merc myself. Still, if they were giving one of those away…' His angular mouth split into a grin. 'Who is he?'

'Where's Mrs Barnet?' Cathy asked sharply. She swept worriedly through the hallway.

'The old woman? Oh, she's still here. Wouldn't leave. I tried telling her that I'm an old friend, but she's a stubborn sort—reminds me a lot of my old gran.' Gary grinned. '*She* didn't like me either.'

'Mrs Barnet!' Cathy walked into the living room, relieved to see her next-door neighbour sitting placidly in front of the television. 'Is everything OK? Robbie—?'

'He's fine.' The old woman raised herself awkwardly from the armchair. 'Hasn't stirred all evening. I let this…' she paused, glancing towards Gary as if she couldn't decide how to describe him '…young man in about ten minutes ago. He frightened the life out of me, he did, what with his motorbike and his banging. He assured me he was a friend of yours, and then I remembered I had seen him helping you move in, so…' The wrinkled face creased into a frown. 'I hope I did right?'

'Yes…of course you did.' Cathy managed a smile. She wondered how she was supposed to get through the next few minutes without bursting into floods of tears. She hardened her expression and looked across at Gary, who was now sitting on the arm of the chair. He was wearing a black leather biking jacket and torn denims, and both garments looked as if they should have been thrown out long ago. 'I think you owe Mrs Barnet an apology. You should have had a little more thought.'

'Yeah…well…sorry if I frightened you, but I wasn't to know you'd be here.' Gary looked at Cathy, sharp hazel eyes appraising the outfit she wore. 'Where have you been, anyway, dressed like that?'

'Oh…it was just a village thing…' Cathy shook her head. The ball was the last thing she wanted to be reminded of.

'Did you have a good time, dear?' Mrs Barnet smiled happily at Cathy.

'Perfect.' Cathy's voice was tight with emotion. 'Well, Mrs Barnet,' she added swiftly, 'I'm sure you must be wanting to get home.'

The old woman nodded in agreement. 'Yes, dear, I think I'll leave you youngsters to it.' She threw a disapproving frown in Gary's direction.

'Bit uptight, aren't you?' Gary commented, once Mrs Barnet had left. 'Who was he, by the way—anyone I should know?'

'Don't start, Gary!'

'Are you and he an item?'

'That's none of your business.' Cathy's voice was terse.

'Ah! So you are!' Gary, unperturbed by her tone, sounded gleeful. 'You'll do well keeping in with 'im. Loaded, if that car was anything to go by!' The angular mouth split into a harsh grin. 'D'you think he'd fancy helping out a chap in need of a few quid?' Gary turned towards her and his face was alight with the prospect of easy money.

Cathy frowned in horror. 'Are you mad?'

'Come on! A couple of hundred…it's pocket money to a man like that—loose change. And if you said that you were a bit short…' Gary glanced around the room. 'He must see how things are—'

'I can't believe you're asking me to do this!' Cathy blazed, as all the tension of the evening came to a head. 'What do you think I am—some kind of parasite? Do you think I'm even remotely interested in his money?' She shook her head as tears welled up in her eyes. 'I wish he were poor! I wish he didn't have a penny to his name! I wish he were just like me so that we could help each other as equals—' She broke off as the tears threatened to overwhelm her.

'All right! Calm down!' Gary flopped down on the settee. 'What's he done—offered to pay for a meal?'

'I don't want to talk about it.' Cathy flipped off her shoes and began heading towards the stairs.

'That's it, isn't it?' Gary replied. 'He's got loads of money, but you want him to be poor like the rest of us! My God! Talk about perverse! Most women can't wait to find some rich devil to make their life a little easier, but not you. Oh, no! Cathy Taylor's got 'er principles!'

'Well, I'd rather have some than none at all!' Cathy turned with tears in her eyes. She would never forget the way Daniel had looked at her in the car: sort of sad and cold and regretful, not angry and hating her, as she had half expected. 'I'll go and find you a blanket. But if you think for one moment...' She shook her head as the tears threatened to overwhelm her. 'Forget it, Gary!' she told him firmly. 'Just forget it!'

'Mummy, why is Gary here? I can't watch my television programmes.'

'Why can't you?'

'He won't let me have the remote.' Robbie snuggled under the bedcovers. He felt cold. Cathy turned towards him and hugged him close.

'Never mind, darling. Stay here with me. You shouldn't be watching television at this hour anyway.'

'Why is he here again?'

Cathy was wondering the same thing. 'Oh, I don't know. Because he just wanted to see us, I suppose,' she murmured.

'I don't like Gary. He's not like Daniel. Daniel always wants to talk to me. Will we see him today, d'you think?'

'No.' Cathy's reply was firm. 'Not today.'

'When?'

'Please, Robbie, go back to sleep. It's very early, and I'm tired.'

But Robbie was in the mood to talk. 'Did you know Daniel's mummy and daddy live in that very big house?

Do you think we'll be able to go there soon? I want to climb the trees. They're very big.'

'You knew?' Cathy inhaled a breath. 'How did you…?' She could barely speak. The pain of losing Daniel was like a knife twisting in her heart.

'Oh, Tom at school said about it,' Robbie explained. He snuggled close against Cathy's body. 'Daniel's very lucky, isn't he? To have a garden almost as big as the *world*…'

Later, once Robbie had fallen back to sleep in her arms, Cathy slipped out of bed. She couldn't lie there any longer, going over and over all that had happened. She had dozed fitfully for a while, but dreams of Daniel had jerked her awake and back to reality.

What have I done? she thought. Why have I insisted on making myself so miserable? She could hear the television blaring downstairs. Gary's presence wasn't helping any.

He was sprawled on the settee watching television and smoking a cigarette when she went down. There was a coffee mug on the floor and a saucer, acting as an ashtray, on his lap. Her newly decorated room smelt badly of smoke.

'Gary, this isn't going to work.' She marched to the windows and opened them wide. 'I've put you up for one night, but you must have realised that this isn't a good time for me.'

'You said come over any time.' He sounded belligerent.

'Did I?' Cathy frowned, trying to remember. She had been so euphoric at the prospect of living here that she might have said anything. 'Well, yes, I know, but that was before your last visit—'

'Ah, so you didn't mean it. Not a very nice attitude to take with someone who helped you to move in, is it?'

Cathy stared at Gary. She didn't like his tone. In fact she didn't like very much about him at all just at the moment. He had changed, and not for the better either. 'You're in real trouble, aren't you?' she asserted. 'Why don't you just tell me what's wrong, then maybe I might be more inclined to help you?'

'I don't need your help!'

'Well, what's this if it's not help?' Cathy picked up the dirty plate and cup on the table in front of him. 'You know I haven't got any money, Gary. I'm living on a shoestring as it is—'

'You gave me a tenner the other day.'

'Yes, and it just about broke me.' Cathy thought about Robbie's birthday money in the tin upstairs in her wardrobe. There was no way she would give Gary that—it was for Robbie, and she was determined he was going to have at least one decent present on his birthday. 'Do you still owe people—is that it?' A thought flashed into Cathy's mind. 'Are they looking for you? Is that why you're here? Is that why you hid your motorbike around the back of the house last night?' She dragged a hand through her auburn hair, sensing that she had got it right. 'Oh, Gary!' she cried. 'How could you?'

'Don't panic! They're not going to look here.'

'They?' Cathy's heart lurched. *'They?'* she repeated. 'Someone *is* after you.' She closed her eyes for a moment in utter despair. 'That's it! You're going to have to go! I've got Robbie to consider. I can maybe manage to give you a little money, but you're going to have to be on your way. Look…I'll take Robbie out for a walk. But when I get back…' Cathy went to her bag and pulled out her purse. 'Here's another ten pounds.' She held it out to him. 'I'm sorry, but I can't afford any more.'

'What the hell am I supposed to do with this?' Gary's expression was hard.

Cathy made as if to put the money back in her handbag, but he snatched it from her before she could do so.

'Do you have any idea how much I owe?' he continued. 'This won't even cover the interest for a week!'

'Gary…' Cathy shook her head. Robbie entered the room. He had dressed himself, putting his sweatshirt on back to front again as usual. 'Look…' she murmured, lowering her voice. 'This isn't my problem. I've got enough to deal with as it is! I told you months ago not to get mixed up with those so-called mates of yours…' Cathy inhaled a steadying breath. 'Steve did, and look how he ended up.'

'Which is where I'll most probably be if I don't get my hands on some money pronto!' Gary responded harshly. 'Go for your walk, then,' he continued. 'I'll go. I know when I've outstayed my welcome!'

His bike had disappeared when Cathy and Robbie returned from feeding the ducks. Cathy gave a huge sigh of relief as she let herself into the house and saw that Gary's few possessions had gone and the settee was back to being a settee again instead of a bed.

'Will Gary come back again?' Robbie asked, as he scrabbled about in a drawer for his sketchpad. 'I hope not. I don't like the way he smells—all smoky and dirty. Daniel doesn't smell like that. He smells nice. Is he coming to see us today?'

Cathy hesitated, debating whether it wouldn't be for the best to tell Robbie straight out. 'Well…I'm not sure, exactly. He's a very busy man.'

Robbie settled himself at the kitchen table with his crayons. 'Well, we could go and see him then. Do you think Daniel will let us visit the very big house? They've got big, big trees. I could climb right to the top!'

'You could not!' Cathy ruffled his hair. 'Anyway, Mummy would worry if you went too high!'

'No…no you wouldn't.' Robbie turned to her with a serious eye. ''Cos I'd be safe if Daniel were there to help me…'

He hadn't slept for two nights. The sunrise had been spectacular, but without Cathy in his life it had meant nothing. This couldn't be happening, he thought, as he crossed the fields towards Langforde Hall. One moment he had been the happiest man alive, and now…

His family home looked majestic in the sunlight. The lush green gardens, offset by the formal symmetry of the building, were bursting with colour and life. It was going to be a gorgeous day, and that somehow made everything seem worse.

Daniel released a misty breath. He had managed to finish the painting of her, but it had been an extremely painful experience. Afterwards, he had really wallowed in self-pity, retrieving the engagement ring from the safe in his study, sitting, staring at it for a long, long while, imagining how things might have been if he'd had the good sense to be straight with Cathy from the start.

What would she make now of the diamond ring which he had bought so happily in London? he wondered. Not much. He tried to picture the likely scene. Hell, Cathy would take one look at the size of the stone and throw the damned thing back in his face! It had cost…well, enough money to keep her and Robbie in the style to which they had unfortunately become accustomed for the best part of ten years.

Was his wealth obscene? It was a question he had asked himself over and over, ever since Cathy had rejected him so forcibly. Perhaps, but there was more to it than that. Tangled in amongst the mess of the moment was the fact that he had lied to her and deceived her so effectively; that was what she objected so strongly about—and how could he blame her for thinking badly of him when he felt so badly of himself?

The men were already erecting the various marquees for the day ahead. If the weather held—Daniel glanced up at the cloudless sky—and it certainly looked like doing that, then the country fair would bring a massive crowd.

He tilted his head towards the morning sun. Thousands upon thousands of people attending from miles around, and the only person who mattered to him would not be there…

CHAPTER TEN

'Mummy, mummy! Why are you crying?'

Cathy hastily dried her tears with the back of her hand and thrust the tin underneath the bedclothes. 'Oh, I'm just being silly. Take no notice of me,' she murmured. She inhaled a huge, steadying breath and managed a smile. 'Ready for a game? Have you brushed your teeth properly after breakfast?'

Robbie bared two rows of neat white teeth for inspection. 'Are they sparkly?'

'Very sparkly.' Cathy looked at her son's dear little face and it was all she could do to keep from bursting into another torrent of tears. 'Good boy,' she murmured shakily. 'Go and hide, then, before I finish counting...'

He touched her arm then, bending low so that he could look into her face. 'Are you really all right, Mummy?' Robbie asked, suddenly sounding so grown up that Cathy was transported goodness knows how many years into the future. It was almost too much in this moment to imagine her son as a man, concerned once again for whatever mess she had managed to get herself into.

Cathy stroked his cheek tenderly. 'Yes, sweetheart. Now off you go.' She began counting down from fifty and Robbie scampered off, determined to be hidden safely before zero.

After he had skipped along the landing, Cathy got up and put the tin back on the top shelf of her wardrobe. It rattled faintly. Gary had been generous, she thought with a bitter smile. He hadn't taken everything; there was almost three pounds left in loose change. Enough, if she were lucky, to buy Robbie a card and a toy car for his birthday.

Damn Gary! Hate surged through her body. How dared he do this!

She remembered she was supposed to be counting. Her voice quivered as she reached twenty and she had to make a concerted effort to keep from breaking down completely.

What was she going to do? A small voice inside her head mentioned Daniel's name, but she thrust the obvious away with a disgusted shake of her head. That wasn't an option, not now; asking Daniel for money, even if it was in the form of a loan, didn't bear thinking about. She knew why he had kept his wealth a secret from her. He didn't trust her, imagined she was some kind of gold-digger—to go now and ask him for money, especially after the ball... Cathy shook her head. She couldn't do it. She had her pride, her dignity, and besides, it was her own stupid fault for trusting Gary, for allowing someone with his track record into her home...

Cathy shouted out zero loudly, so Robbie would hear, then wandered into her workroom to look for him. An idea occurred to her as her eyes ranged over the various boxes scattered on the floor. She needed to sort this mess out for herself. She had been the one foolish enough to allow Gary into her home; she couldn't let Robbie suffer because of it.

What time was it? Still quite early. Cathy remembered what Daniel had said about the country fair—of course at the time, she had had no idea of the connection he had with it, but she mustn't dwell on that aspect now...

There were a good amount of bird boxes and garden tidies, and a half-decent quantity of painted wooden plant labels. Cathy delved into the box and picked out a set. She splayed each label in her hand like a fan of cards. This one was for an assortment of herbs. She read each one: mint, thyme, basil... They were waterproof; that was something. Cathy wiped her tears from the indelible lettering, scurried along the landing to where she suspected Robbie was hiding, and tried not to think about the heart-aching prospect of seeing Daniel again.

*   *   *

'Excellent day for it!' Daniel's father fell into step beside him. 'Good turn-out, as usual. Did Samuel check that sheep, d'you know? It looked distinctly dodgy to me, I mentioned it to Geoff when they were first unloaded, but you know how precious he can be about his livestock.' There was a slight pause. 'Daniel?'

'Sorry...' Daniel collected his thoughts. 'What were you saying?'

'Oh, nothing of particular importance.' His father, looking every inch the country gentleman in a tweed hacking jacket and plus-fours, waved his shooting stick in the direction of the livestock section. 'Just blithering on about sheep.' They walked in silence for a few moments. 'Is everything all right? You don't seem...well, quite with it.'

'No, I'm not. I haven't had much sleep for a couple of nights.'

Daniel focused his gaze on the various stalls as they passed by. It was still early, almost an hour to go before they opened up the grounds to the public, but already the vast majority of them were occupied with people busy setting up their wares.

'Doesn't sound too promising. Presumably it has something to do with that girl—the one you were looking for at the ball? Your mother put two and two together—she worked out that you and she are...involved.'

'Were.' Daniel's voice held no emotion. 'Were involved,' he repeated, almost as a way of torturing himself. He stopped and thrust his hands into the pockets of his trousers. It was a beautiful morning, crisp and bright with the promise of warm sunshine to come. 'She doesn't want to have anything more to do with me.'

'I see.' His father looked into Daniel's face, then away again, focusing deliberately on the horizon. 'She has a son, I believe?'

'Father, you can stop pretending.' Daniel turned and looked down into the craggy, distinguished face. 'I know Mother will have found out everything there is to know about Cathy and that she'll be more than a little relieved when you tell her that our relationship is not in the best of shape.'

'She was bound to mention the child.'

Daniel's expression hardened. 'Of course!'

'Now, Daniel, you're being unfair. Your mother only wants what's best for you—'

Daniel's mouth twisted into a smile. He didn't want to get into the age-old argument—not now. 'Yes,' he replied dryly, 'so she keeps saying.'

'What exactly is the trouble between you and...?' His father hesitated.

'Cathy,' Daniel replied, in the neutral tones which had served him so well ever since the preparations for the fair had begun in earnest. 'Her name's Cathy.'

'Cathy. Yes, of course. So...what was—*is* the trouble?' His father smiled awkwardly. 'Of course, if you'd rather not talk about it—'

Daniel frowned, surprised by his father's interest. 'Money,' he stated flatly. 'And before you and mother breathe a sigh of relief at my lucky escape, the problem happens to be the exact opposite of what you're thinking.'

'The opposite?'

Daniel nodded. 'Ironic, isn't it? Cathy preferred me when she thought I was a poor, struggling artist with barely a penny to my name.' He heard the mockery in his own voice and winced. God, he sounded so...hateful.

'When she thought...?' Daniel's father looked puzzled. 'But where did she get that idea from...?' He glanced at his son's expression. *'You?'*

Daniel released a breath. Perhaps discussing this with his father was not the best of ideas. 'The whole thing came about through accident, rather than by design,' he explained briefly. 'Money, as Mother will have no doubt discovered, is the bane of Cathy's life—she's acutely aware of how little she's got.' Daniel's lips twisted into a tortured smile. 'When we first met...' He shook his head as he remembered. 'Suffice it to say she thought I was a kindred spirit and I simply chose not to enlighten her.'

'Dangerous, given the village aptitude for gossip,' his father replied in even tones.

'Oh, I know I've acted like a complete and utter idiot!' Daniel released a taut breath. 'But at the time it felt like the right thing to do. If I'd have known…' He shook his head. 'I had no idea how quickly we'd…how I'd feel about her—' He changed tack. 'She's so…courageous,' he continued, speaking mostly to himself. 'Strong…determined—'

'And she has her pride.'

Daniel looked at his father, surprised that he should have got to the essence of the disaster so quickly. 'Yes,' he agreed. 'She certainly has that. She's made it perfectly clear she doesn't want to have anything more to do with me.' Daniel looked for relief in his father's eyes and was faintly pleased when he saw none.

'And you have yours. Which is why you're standing here now, looking utterly miserable.' The grey head shook slightly. 'Daniel, I've never known you let something important defeat you before—this *is* important?' his father queried. 'I'm not reading the situation wrongly, am I?'

'No, you're not.' Daniel's voice was firm. 'But she needs time—at least…' He frowned. 'I'm hoping that's what she needs.'

She nearly cried at the sight of him. Her nerves were on edge. Her whole body ached with wanting him. She had been half-dreading, half-looking forward to seeing him again, and now here he was, standing less than forty feet away, looking just wonderful. Her eyes wandered over his muscular frame, clad now in logan-green shirt and black corduroy trousers. He was talking to his father, and he looked so serious and handsome and—

Cathy quickly averted her gaze as Daniel glanced over towards the tall wrought-iron gates which marked the en-

trance to the estate and saw her. She tucked her ticket into
the pocket of her jeans, thanked the man on the gate who
had given her directions to her numbered stall, and tried to
walk away as quickly as she could.

'Cathy…!'

Daniel's dark eyes ranged over the vision before him.
She wondered that he didn't laugh aloud—for she knew
she must make a pretty ridiculous picture; other stall-
holders had no doubt arrived in a variety of vehicles,
whereas Cathy felt akin to a Sherpa, laden as she was with
suitcases and boxes and a very heavy haversack.

'Let me help you with something.' Daniel reached forward and made as if to take the suitcase from her hand, but
Cathy stubbornly refused to relinquish her hold.

'I'm fine!' she replied stiffly. 'I've carried everything all
the way from home, I'm sure I can take manage a few steps
further.'

He looked at her then, and his gaze spoke volumes—far
better than any words. Cathy cursed inwardly. She hadn't
meant to sound quite so horrible. Oh, hell! Why couldn't
she just give in and accept that she needed him?

'What are you doing here? Sorry, stupid question!' he
continued, glancing at the boxes she was struggling with.
'But, Cathy, you weren't planning on attending. You told
me so yourself. This is rather a last-minute decision, isn't
it?'

'A little like the one you took when you finally told me
about all this!' Cathy responded sharply. 'Oh, no,' she
added, 'that's not right, is it? I found out by accident, didn't
I? When I saw you standing with your mother and father
looking every inch the aristocrat!'

He looked *so* angry. Perhaps that was for the best, she
thought. If she infuriated him, made him hate her, then
maybe he would give up and put her out of her misery.

'I'm not going to argue with you, so you may as well
save your breath.' His words were clipped. Daniel reached

forward and determinedly removed the suitcase from Cathy's grasp.

She glared at him—she had to do something; it was either glare or burst into tears, and that wouldn't help her predicament. Not in the slightest. 'The man at the gate said my stall is somewhere over on the far side of the field,' she announced.

'Let me see your ticket.' Daniel waited whilst Cathy removed the ticket from her pocket, then looked at the number. 'This is no good,' he continued. 'It's miles away. You won't sell a thing. Follow me.' Daniel led the way along the line of traders who were all busy setting up their stalls, until he came to an empty stand, situated slap bang in the middle of the main arena. 'This is better.'

Cathy looked around her. It was in a marvellous position near to a thoroughfare, so that lots of people would pass by and hopefully stop to look at the goods she had for sale.

'I was a late applicant...' Cathy murmured. 'I don't deserve such a good position.' She looked up into Daniel's face. 'What about the person destined for this spot? Won't you have to give them some sort of compensation?'

'I'll deal with it.' Daniel's gaze was cool. 'So, you *are* going to accept my offer of help, then?'

'Yes.' Cathy thought of the huge amount missing from Robbie's birthday tin. 'I am.' She risked a brief smile, which wasn't, she found, such a good idea, because softening her outer shell meant crumbling on the inside, and she couldn't afford to do that—not right now anyway. 'Thank you—very much,' she added stiffly.

'My pleasure.' She'd expected a sardonic edge to his voice, but there was none. 'If you'd like help setting up...?' Cathy shook her head, and was relieved when Daniel didn't push it. 'How's Robbie, by the way?' he asked.

She heaved a steadying breath. 'He's fine...thank you. He's with Mrs Barnet. The two of them are going to come along later.'

'That's good.' Daniel's brief smile showed he was genuinely pleased. 'There's a small funfair and a farm for younger children, even an obstacle course if he's feeling adventurous...' He paused. 'Cathy—'

'Daniel, don't!' She lowered her head, busying herself with unpacking her wares. 'We've said all there is to say.'

'Why are you here?'

'To sell—why else?' She forced herself to look into his face. 'I decided I might as well get rid of some of the stuff which was cluttering up the spare room...'

'You know you can always come to me if you've got a problem, don't you?' Daniel murmured quietly.

'Why should I have a problem?' She knew she sounded defensive. Cathy met his gaze, struggling to brazen it out. If Daniel only knew what Gary had done...

'I don't like to think of you struggling alone. You'll come to me,' he persisted, 'if you need help?'

It was almost as if he could read her mind. 'Money, do you mean?' Cathy asked, hating the hardness in her voice.

'There are other ways; you know that.' Daniel's gaze was admirably placid, given the fact, Cathy thought, that she seemed intent on provoking him beyond all reason. He reached forward and lifted a painted plant holder from the box. 'How long do you intend being like this?'

Cathy glanced sideways, aware that the two of them were under scrutiny from several interested stall-holders. 'Being like what?' she asked.

'You're not going to forgive me, are you?'

Cathy struggled to keep her expression composed. She wanted to throw herself into his arms, to feel the strength and warmth of his body next to hers. A vivid image of their lovemaking flashed into her mind, but she thrust it away and focused instead on the impressive view over Daniel's left shoulder. 'Your family home looks rather beautiful in the sunshine, doesn't it?' she commented pointedly. 'Has it been used for one of those costume dramas on television yet?'

How can you be this way? A small voice screamed inside

her head, even as she spoke the last words. *Don't you love him? Don't you wish you could be with him for the rest of your life?* She did; that was the trouble. But the practical, pessimistic side of herself always won the day. This is for the best, she told herself. End it now before you get hurt any more...

'Do you want me to apologise for being wealthy? Is that it?' Daniel demanded roughly. 'If so, then perhaps you should do the same for being poor!'

'Don't be ridiculous!' Cathy retorted heatedly. 'I'll do no such thing!' She was near to tears. 'Why should I? I wasn't the one who lied, and deceived, and pretended to be somebody I wasn't!'

'You really don't give a damn, do you?' he murmured quietly. His mouth curved slightly, but there was little sign of amusement in his smile. 'And there was I thinking...'

She wasn't about to find out what he had thought. Cathy looked into Daniel's face and saw then that she had finally accomplished her goal—he really did look as if he hated her...

He turned away sharply and she watched him stride off in the direction of the house.

Cathy knew how much she had taken in the last two hours and it didn't amount to very much. She had had such high hopes of, if not selling everything, then at least reducing her stock by half. She gazed about her stall. The things which had sold well had been the low-priced items, such as the labels and the wooden garden signs—not nearly expensive enough, even in quantity, to cover the amount which Gary had stolen from her.

What was she going to do? She wanted to cry again. It was a constant battle to keep a composed expression. She had caught glimpses of Daniel from time to time, but they had been rare, and on each occasion he had been in the company of a variety of different personages—some from the village and others, Cathy supposed, from further afield.

'How much is this?' A middle-aged woman in a Hermès headscarf and bottle-green padded jacket, who had been regarding Cathy's display for the last few minutes, looked up from the bird box she was examining and smiled when Cathy told her the price. 'It's charming,' she commented smoothly. 'I'd like three, please. Also…' She scanned the stall quickly. 'One of these—an apron, is it?'

'Actually, it's for the shed or workshop, or wherever,' Cathy explained, dragging her gaze away from Daniel's figure. She unfolded the item and held it up. 'It's a tidying device. The pockets are for seeds, or string, or tools—whatever happens to be lying around.'

'Ah!' The woman beamed. 'Yes, that will be fine. Thank you. I'll take two.'

She handed over three twenty-pound notes. Cathy delved in her money bag for the small amount of change required and felt her spirits lift a little as she wrapped the items.

Things got better from then on—in terms of sales at least. Over the next hour Cathy managed to sell nearly all of her stock. She felt relieved. The day had been a trial, and she felt desperately miserable, but at least she had managed to replace virtually all the money Gary had stolen from her.

'Hetty, would you mind watching my stall for a few moments?' After a long morning, Cathy was on first-name terms with the adjacent stall-holder, a friendly woman in her fifties from outside the area, who was selling beautiful soft toys and babywear which she knitted herself. 'I promised my son and neighbour I'd meet them by the barbecue.'

'Sure, my dear. Off you go.'

There was quite a queue for sausages and burgers and roast venison. Cathy looked around for Robbie and spied him at the front of the queue, standing beside Mrs Barnet, eagerly accepting a large hamburger.

'Mummy!' He waved cheerfully and came rushing over. 'Can I have a go on the funfair?' His face was alight with excitement. 'They've got a roundabout with painted horses.'

'Of course you can.' Cathy took hold of her son's hand and smiled at Mrs Barnet, who came towards her at a more sedentary pace. 'Let's find a quiet spot so you can eat first, shall we?'

Cathy led the way to a shady position beneath some trees. It was after one o'clock and the day had grown increasingly warm. She slipped off her cardigan as she sat beside Robbie and tried not to think of Daniel, still unable to reconcile the fact that this was his family home. Imagine living *here*, she thought, glancing around at the acres of parkland. She shielded her eyes against the sun and looked towards the glint of a lake in the distance, at the wooded area beyond and then right towards the house.

There he was! A thrill of awareness, then pain on recognition, twisted like a knife in her stomach. Daniel was standing across the plain of grass which separated the stalls from the roped off area near to the house, chatting to the woman who had bought so much from Cathy's stall earlier in the morning. He had sunglasses on now and looked even more handsome, more glamorous, more wealthy, more unattainable…

The woman handed over the carrier bag she was holding and Daniel took it. Cathy looked harder. The distinctive yellow-patterned scarf glinted in the sunshine. No, she hadn't been mistaken, it *was* the same woman, and her carrier bag was the one she had given the woman from her stall. Why, then, was she passing it over to Daniel…?

A curious thought embedded itself in Cathy's mind and wouldn't be dislodged, no matter how hard she tried to reason it away—in fact the more she thought the harder it was to dismiss her idea as pure folly. Cathy cast her mind back to the sudden increase in sales and knew her instincts were correct. She had thought it curious that just a few customers over a short period of time had wanted to buy in bulk. Forty pounds here, sixty there—she'd never had sales as good as that before.

Anger surged through her veins as she looked across at

Daniel and the woman. It couldn't be coincidence. How could he do this? she thought furiously. How did he dare to be so...so patronising, especially knowing the way things stood between them?

Cathy rose to her feet. 'Mrs Barnet, could I leave you with Robbie?' she murmured distractedly. 'Only, there's somebody I need to speak to...'

She marched purposefully; her legs felt like jelly and her heart was racing fit to burst, but she persevered across the smooth, gently undulating lawn which led towards the rear of the house.

'Too grand to buy things for yourself?' She looked pointedly down at the carrier bag Daniel was holding. 'Those *are* my bird boxes, I take it?' she queried acidly.

He looked directly into her face, cool, dark eyes assessing the fury in Cathy's expression. 'They are, yes.'

'Well, what do you think you're doing with them?' she demanded. 'I didn't sell them to *you*.'

The woman in the headscarf looked startled. 'I apologise for Cathy's rather abrupt manner,' Daniel drawled smoothly. His mouth twisted into a smile. 'I didn't realise until recently, but underneath that deceptively placid exterior she has the most incredibly fiery temper.'

'Don't patronise me—not on top of everything else!' It was all Cathy could do not to spit out the words. 'Why?' she gritted. 'Why?'

He looked infuriatingly cool and collected. 'Because I wanted to help.'

'How...how could you?' Cathy cried out in frustration. 'Do you have no idea how to treat me?'

'Clearly not.' Daniel's tone was curt. 'I seem to make mistakes at every turn. Margaret—' he turned to the woman at his side, '—would you excuse us?'

Cathy watched as the woman thankfully scurried away. 'Do you actually *want* those bird boxes?' she queried shakily, glancing at the bag. 'You *did* give that woman money to buy them for you, didn't you? And what about the others? It's no coincidence, is it, that I've had such a steady stream of customers?'

'If I had come and purchased items directly, would you have sold them to me?' Daniel asked. Cathy's expression was taut with emotion. 'No, I thought not. And, yes, I do happen to want some of these things. Maybe not quite so many, but—'

'You see! Just charity!' Cathy's green eyes blazed. 'Haven't you worked it out by now?' she blazed. 'I don't want your damned charity! I have my pride—'

'Oh, yes! Your *pride*!' All at once the tension within Daniel's frame seemed to snap free. He reached out and held Cathy by the arm. She could feel the pressure of his fingers tight around her wrist. 'How could I forget about that precious commodity?' He shook his head, oblivious, or so it seemed, of the interested glances of passers-by. 'Is that what stops you from saying how you really feel? It must be, because I can't believe you're as cold and as heartless as you make out!' He paused, and dark, dangerous eyes seared her face as he pulled her closer towards him. There was steel in his voice when he next spoke. 'I can remember how you were when we made love, even if you choose not to!' he told her huskily.

Cathy looked up into his face for a long time, fighting against the desires and emotions which assailed her body. How was she ever going to live without this man? She loved him *so* much. 'That's not fair! How...how can you remind me of that now?' she croaked.

'Fair?' There was a mocking hardness in his voice. 'When is life ever fair? And why shouldn't I remind you of how loving and passionate and totally uninhibited you were?'

Her fingers made contact with his face before she had time to think. She had to stop him saying such things— even if every word he said was true—and this, for an infinitesimal moment of time, seemed the only way. A mistake, though. Immediately her palm had connected with his cheek she knew that. Cathy, staring at Daniel in dismay, curled her fingers into a tight ball, drawing her raised hand away as if in slow motion. Misty emerald eyes scanned the red weal on his face.

'Do you feel better now?' His eyes were full of danger.

'I didn't mean—'

'Perhaps we should go somewhere, continue this conversation in more appropriate surroundings, out of the glare of the public eye.'

'I don't want to go anywhere with you!' Cathy cried. 'Daniel—!'

He wasn't listening. She saw in a moment the heat of anger surging within his body, felt the strength of it as he lifted her clear of the ground and swung her into his arms.

'Put me down! Stop this!' Cathy hissed. 'Daniel, what on earth do you think you're doing?'

'Something which I should have done the night of the ball!' he replied roughly.

'If you think this macho man image cuts any ice with me—!' Cathy spluttered.

'Macho...?' Daniel shook his head. He didn't look in the least bit amused. 'You were the one who hit me— remember?'

Cathy wiped a hand over her eyes. They were headed for Langforde Hall. 'You provoked me!' She glanced up at the creamy Georgian edifice. 'I don't want to go in that house ever again,' she cried.

'Tough!' Daniel was clearly in no mood to be argued with.

'What are you trying to do?' Cathy enquired shakily. 'Humiliate me even further?'

Daniel's feet crunched across the gravel and ascended the sweeping stone steps. 'Just save your energy and be quiet.'

It was cool and quiet inside. Cathy struggled with a myriad of emotions as Daniel carried her across the vast expanse of tiled hallway. He pushed open a door. Cathy released a shaky sigh. The room was very elegant; there were silken drapes in shades of mint-green and cream, a chaise longue and a matching striped sofa which was almost the size of a double bed. 'Now!' Daniel clicked the door shut. 'Now you can tell me what you really think of me. Come on! Don't hold back.' His voice was ragged with emotion. 'I really want to hear—all of it.'

'Don't bully me.' Cathy swallowed, and felt the tightness in her throat. 'I don't want things to end this way.'

'But you want them to end?'

Cathy's heart twisted painfully in her chest. She should say yes, now—right now—but she couldn't do it. Instead she said, 'You were kind; you felt sorry for me.'

Daniel's eyes sparked fire. 'Who says?'

'No one says. I...I just know that's the way it was.'

'Sandra?' Daniel glanced into Cathy's reddened face, then spun away, pacing the room with angry strides. 'Oh, I might have guessed she'd plant a few insidious ideas in your head. She's jealous. Surely you can see that!'

'It doesn't mean that what she said isn't true,' Cathy murmured miserably.

'And what exactly *did* she say?' Daniel demanded.

'I don't want to tell you.'

'Don't you think I have a right to know—considering her words have so clearly had an effect? Although why you should take any notice of what a desperate and devious woman like Sandra should say, I've no idea! She's a gold-digger—'

'And you have to protect yourself from those sort of people, don't you?' Cathy murmured quietly.

Daniel stopped pacing. 'That's what you think?'

'I'm just being realistic!' Cathy's voice held a tortured note. 'Can't you understand that? I suppose if I try and put myself in your position—'

'No!' Daniel came towards her, gripped her by both shoulders. 'No,' he repeated, looking into her eyes. 'Don't even begin to believe that.'

'But if it's the truth—'

'Is your regard of me *so* low?' Daniel questioned quietly. 'When we were making love…' His dark head shook at the memory. 'Didn't you *feel* how much I wanted you?'

'Yes, but…but…' Cathy could hardly put her thoughts into words.

'Now you hate me?'

'I don't hate you.' Cathy's voice was small.

'No?' Daniel didn't bother to hide his disbelief.

'I don't hate you,' Cathy repeated. 'Not at all.' She looked down at her hands. 'Quite…quite the opposite, in fact.'

'The opposite…?' Daniel's frown was fiercer than ever.

'It won't work, of course!' Cathy continued swiftly. 'Even if by some miracle you happened to feel the same way, it wouldn't work…' Her voice trailed to a miserable halt. 'It wouldn't work…' she repeated.

'Why wouldn't it?' He sounded harsh. It hardly inspired confidence to continue. 'Cathy, look at me!' Daniel lifted her face with one hand. The heat of his touch scorched her skin. He stared down at her wordlessly for what seemed an eternity. When he eventually spoke, his voice was deep and very husky. 'You have to believe that if I had the chance to go back I'd handle everything differently.'

'By not getting involved with me, do you mean?' Cathy asked briskly.

'Are you being deliberatly obtuse?' Daniel enquired gently. 'Or does it come naturally?' He inhaled a ragged breath. 'Is it so difficult to believe that I should want you with every fibre of my being—body and soul?'

There was a long moment of silence. Cathy stared up into the face of the man she loved in something approaching stupefaction. *What had he just said?* 'Daniel…?' She tried to speak coherently, but her brain wouldn't form the proper words. 'My…my soul…you…you…' Cathy shook her head gently. 'I don't understand. I thought—'

'I love you.'

'Are you sure?' Cathy, frowning slightly, couldn't hide the note of incredulity in her voice.

'More sure of you, of us, than I've ever been of anything in my life before.' His voice was gentle now, strong, but with an underlying edge of emotion which couldn't be ignored.

'Oh, Daniel!' All at once the strength which had sustained Cathy through the last couple of days disintegrated. The misery and tension she had been battling so valiantly against fell in on her. It was all too much, too overwhelming. Cathy's face crumpled. Her body went limp and her knees buckled beneath her. She was crying, then sobbing, the tears falling thick and fast onto her cheeks as she heaved great, racking breaths.

'Cathy? Oh, sweetheart!' Daniel caught her before she fell. His voice was rich with love. She felt the comforting touch of his hand against her hair, the whisper of his lips against her cheek. 'Don't cry, my darling. Please, don't cry...'

But she couldn't stop. Cathy buried her face against his logan shirt, trying in vain to quell the increasing waves of emotion which washed over her. 'I've been so...miserable! And then...then Gary...' She gulped back a sob. 'Gary—'

'What about him?' Daniel's voice was sharp. He placed his hands gently on her hair and, tilting her face towards his, looked deep into her eyes.

'He...he was at the house after you dropped me off. I told him to leave...but he took Robbie's money.' Her voice rose and fell on a wave of disgust.

'What?'

'Robbie's birthday money.' Cathy pressed a hand over her mouth to try and quell the sobs. 'I was saving so that I could buy him a nice present. Gary stole it.'

'He did what?' Daniel cursed violently. 'Where is he now?'

'I don't know.'

'Have you phoned the police?'

'No!' Cathy shook her head. 'I don't want them involved. Please, Daniel!' She looked up at him with anguish
in her eyes. 'Don't tell me I have to involve them!'

'OK. Shh. Don't cry.' Daniel gently led Cathy over to
the chaise longue. 'Stop worrying about the money and
Gary now. Just take a deep breath…there…that's it…shh.'

It was some moments before Cathy regained her composure. 'I must look an awful mess,' she murmured rag-
gedly. 'What on earth do you see in me?'

Daniel's smile was gentle. 'I see everything I've ever
wanted in a woman: strength and sweetness and humour,
compassion and kindness, determination, pride… I love
you, my darling.' He said it so easily, so simply.

Cathy's heart almost burst with happiness. She looked
up into Daniel's face. 'You really do?' she whispered.

'Absolutely.' A smile crept across his gorgeous mouth.
'I love you,' he repeated. 'More than anything in the
world.'

'Are you…sure?' she asked, frowning a little, because
she still didn't trust herself enough to believe that something as wonderful as this was actually happening. 'I
mean…' She sniffed, gulped another couple of breaths.
'You don't have to say it just to make me feel better—'

'I love you,' Daniel repeated. 'Believe it.' He kissed her
trembling mouth very gently. 'Now don't start crying
again,' he warned. 'Or you'll have me in tears too! I never
meant to hurt you, Cathy—not today, with my crazy idea
to buy up half of your stall, not before, when I chose not
to tell you about my wealth. Please say we can work this
thing out.'

'You really…love me?' Cathy tried not to labour the
point, but the trouble was she still couldn't quite believe it.

'Don't.' His voice was mild. He seemed to enjoy looking
at her, content to allow his gaze to roam over every inch
of her.

Cathy sniffed. 'Don't what?' she asked.

'Don't doubt anything I've said.' He swept back a strand

of hair from her face. 'I love every inch of you. I love your stubbornness and your pride. I love the way you smile and the way you walk…' Daniel's mouth curved into a stunning smile. 'I even love that look in your eyes when you're as mad as hell!'

Cathy began to feel as if the weight of the world were being lifted from her shoulders. 'Not that, surely?' she queried lightly. 'I must look like a demon!'

'Pretty much,' Daniel agreed. He looked serious suddenly. 'So, does my confession alter anything? Is this money thing still going to come between us?' A shadow fell across Cathy's face. 'What?' He looked amazed suddenly. *'It is?'*

'No!' Cathy replied quickly. 'No,' she repeated.

'You sound as if you're trying to convince yourself.' Daniel leaned forward and kissed Cathy's mouth slowly, once, twice, three times. 'Let me do that for you…'

She wanted to drown in his kiss as his mouth moved with slow sensuality over her lips. How could I have ever imagined I could live without him? Cathy asked herself. It didn't matter about his money; she didn't care if he was a dustman or a distinguished member of the aristocracy; all she cared about was Daniel as a person.

She pulled away a little and looked into his eyes, saw the questions lying there, knew that she wanted things to be right from now on. No secrets. No misunderstandings. 'I'm frightened,' she whispered.

Daniel frowned. *'Frightened?'* he repeated. 'Of what?'

'Us.' She saw him shake his head a little, not comprehending. 'Of how we feel about each other,' Cathy continued. 'I haven't told you, have I?' she said suddenly. 'Oh, Daniel, *I love you too!'* Her voice was intense with feeling; her eyes swam with tears. 'I love you *so* much…so much,' she repeated, 'that it hurts.'

'I don't want it to hurt you,' Daniel replied, kissing her mouth very gently. 'Never.'

'What if we…?' Cathy's voice trailed away. She didn't

want to voice her fears, but she knew that she had to so that they could be out in the open, where they could both examine them. 'Our lives have been—are,' she amended, '*so* different.'

'That matters?'

'It might.'

'Not to me,' Daniel asserted.

'The reason I was so…hateful when I found out who you were on the night of the ball was…well, it was really because I was so frightened that you had kept things from me because you didn't trust me, because our relationship was just a fling, that you didn't really want or expect anything from it.'

'Not true.' Daniel spoke quietly. He inhaled a steadying breath. 'Everything happened so fast between us. I was in a daze. One minute I was just a simple bachelor, living alone, worrying about my art, and the next…' His mouth curved into another smile. 'Pow! There you were. You and Robbie.'

'We upset your nice, peaceful existence,' Cathy murmured.

'I'm glad you did—so glad.' He kissed her again, and his mouth was warm and full of passion. 'Cathy, this isn't just a fling. I'm ashamed to say that I've had more than enough of those to last a lifetime.' He looked deep into her eyes. 'I love you. With all my heart.' He stroked a hand along the length of her arm, linking strong fingers with hers. 'Things went wrong that night of the ball. I had very different plans for the both of us, believe me. My train was late, then my mother called…' His dark head shook. 'Events seemed to conspire against me, although I know now that if I had come clean from the very beginning then neither of us would have had to go through this unhappiness.'

'Why didn't you tell me about all this?' Cathy looked around at the room. She had visited a stately home once, trailed round after the guide, admiring the architecture and beautiful furnishings, and now here she was lying in a room which was just as old and just as grand.

'I didn't want to frighten you off. It was as simple as that,' Daniel explained. 'You were clearly struggling along on a small amount of money...' He glanced around. 'I thought mentioning this would rather be like rubbing salt into the wound...and, as I said, everything happened so fast between us. The ironic thing is, I had planned to tell you everything on my return from London.'

'You had?' Cathy's eyes were large and very green.

'Absolutely.'

'Oh!' Cathy clapped a hand to her mouth.

Daniel frowned. 'What is it?'

'Robbie. He's outside with Mrs Barnet. I said I'd only be a few minutes—and there's my stall—Hetty will wonder where I've got to!'

'Hetty?'

'The woman with the stall next to mine.'

Daniel's mouth curved into a delicious smile. 'You feel better now?'

Cathy released a breath and smiled. 'What do you think?'

They were back at Daniel's cottage. Mrs Barnet had been reimbursed, thanked profusely for looking after Robbie and given a lift home.

'...so, then I went on the horse ride, and after that we looked at the goat and the ducks, and then I tried to hit a coconut down, but I kept missing, and then we watched the sheepdogs trying to get all the sheep into the pen, but some of them were naughty and wouldn't go in, and the dogs kept having to go backwards and forwards. I saw one try to bite their ankles.' Robbie finally gulped a breath and closed his eyes. 'Mummy, I like this bedroom. Do you think Daniel will let me play with his toy boat in the morning, if I ask very nicely?'

Cathy bent and kissed her son, pulling the crisp blue and white bedclothes up neatly around his shoulders. 'Mmm, I should think so, darling. Now, how about going to sleep? You've had a very busy day, haven't you? Don't forget, Daniel said he'd help you climb one of those big trees tomorrow at his mummy and daddy's house, so you'll need lots of energy for that.'

'Sounds as if he's had a pretty good time,' Daniel commented with a smile.

'You heard?' Cathy pulled the bedroom door to, leaving it open a little so that the light from the landing illuminated the room.

'I love hearing him talk.'

She smiled. 'You mean that, don't you?'

'Of course! I always mean everything I say.' His lips twisted. 'Well, virtually everything. When I'm mad I have been known to talk complete and utter rubbish.' Daniel kissed Cathy's mouth. 'I'm not mad now, though—far from it. Come with me.' He led her by the hand.

'Where are we going?'

'To my studio. There's something I want to show you.' They climbed up the few stairs which led off from the first floor of the cottage. Daniel opened the door and led Cathy across the wooden floor towards the easel in front of the large north-facing window. 'This is for you.' He lifted the sheet from the canvas and watched as Cathy's gaze fell upon her own portrait.

'Daniel!'

'Do you like it?' He linked strong arms around her waist and held Cathy against his body.

'It's me!'

'Of course it's you.'

'But I look...wonderful!'

'You *are* wonderful.'

Cathy gazed at the painting; she couldn't believe that Daniel had actually done this. She looked positively beautiful, with her halo of fiery red hair and startling green eyes.

'Marry me.'

Cathy looked down in front of her. He was holding out

a small leather box. She stared at it for a moment in amazement, then took it slowly and with trembling fingers lifted
the lid. Silence reigned as Cathy stared down at the most
beautiful diamond ring she had ever set eyes on. It sparkled
in the soft evening light.

'*Oh!*'

'Aren't you going to say anything else?'

It was just as well Daniel was behind her, Cathy thought.
She needed the support of his body after such a shock.
'This...this is for *me*?'

'Only you.'

'I...I don't know what to say.'

'Say yes,' Daniel urged. 'If you don't like the ring then
we'll change it—'

'I love the ring.' Cathy twisted round and looked into
Daniel's handsome face. 'You really want to marry me?'
she whispered. Her mouth curved in surprised delight.
'Truly?'

Daniel lifted her hand and pressed her fingers to his
mouth, and kissed them very slowly, one by one. 'Truly,'
he murmured huskily. 'So?' His dark eyes were as warm
as his kisses. 'Are you going to give me a reply?'

'Yes.' Cathy struggled to keep her voice steady. 'Oh,
Daniel!' she gasped. 'Yes! Yes! Yes!'

EPILOGUE

'THAT was the best picnic I've ever tasted!' Cathy announced. She rested her head back against Daniel's chest and sighed contentedly. 'Martha certainly knows how to make a cucumber sandwich.'

'I think it has more to do with the fact that we haven't had to make them ourselves,' Daniel replied. He stroked a finger against Cathy's cheek. 'The sun's going down. You're not cold?'

'No, not at all.' Cathy snuggled deeper into the layers of woollens, winding Daniel's arm protectively around her extended waist. 'Don't the trees look lovely against the sky?' she murmured sleepily. 'So dark and austere. Don't you think that sky is the very same colour as the roses which were in my bouquet—gold and red, with a touch of yellow?'

'Exactly the same.'

Cathy tipped her head back and looked up into Daniel's strong face. 'You're teasing!' she accused.

'Am I?' His mouth curved deliciously as he dropped a kiss onto her nose. 'I love you,' he murmured.

Cathy raised dark brows. 'Still?' she queried.

'Now who's teasing?' Daniel replied. 'Still,' he confirmed, kissing her again. 'For ever.'

'Your mother called by the cottage today.'

'Did she?'

'We chatted. She told me all about your misdemeanours when you were young.'

'Can't have taken very long, then.'

'She was with me two whole hours! I had no idea you broke your arm when you were six. Which tree was it?'

Daniel considered, then pointed westwards towards the dying sun. 'That one over there, next to the orangery. I was trying to spy on Lem, the old gardener. I was convinced he was some kind of criminal. He used to dodge in the place at odd moments.'

'Really? And was he?'

'No, of course not.' Daniel's voice was light. 'He just used to go in there for a cigarette when he was desperate.'

Cathy glanced down at her lap. 'Robbie's asleep.'

Robbie opened his eyes suddenly. 'No, I'm not!'

'We'd better be getting back soon, darling. You've got school tomorrow.'

She heard him heave a sigh. 'Oh, Mum! I want to hear some more about Daniel breaking his arm.'

'Nothing more to tell, I'm afraid,' he murmured. 'I leaned over too far to try and see what Lem was doing, let go of the branch and fell to the ground. I apparently screamed the place down and Lem came out and found me, and I was whisked off to the cottage hospital.'

'Was there blood?'

'No, 'fraid not.'

'Granny gave me some of your old paints today,' Robbie announced proudly. 'She found them in the attic.' He gazed across at the Hall. 'It must be a 'normous attic,' he mused.

'It is.' Daniel stroked Robbie's hair affectionately. 'I'll take you up there, if you like, and show you around. There are lots of curious bits and pieces.'

'Mrs Collins from the WI asked me if I'd like to judge the daffodils at the spring flower show next week. I was quite taken aback. I know absolutely nothing about them—except that they're cheerful and yellow and they remind me of when Robbie and I first moved here.' Cathy smiled. 'Sweet of her, though.'

'I hope you said no; all that standing around will be too much for you.'

'Don't worry. I politely declined.'

'What does "politely declined" mean?' Robbie asked.

Cathy chuckled. 'It means no, sweetheart.' She adjusted her position, moving a little on the checked rug.

'OK?' Daniel sounded concerned. 'The ground's too hard and it's getting late. We'll go back.'

'You're fussing!' Cathy pronounced lightly. 'You promised me you wouldn't.'

'Did I?' Daniel narrowed his eyes mischievously. 'When? I don't recall.'

'About eight months ago. Approximately a month after our wedding.'

'Our wedding?' Daniel's mouth curved into a delicious smile. 'We got married? The two of us? And after all that commotion about you being poor and me being rich— never!'

Cathy threw him a look. 'Do you want me to tell you all about it?' she asked, grinning broadly. 'Well…it was a beautiful day in June. I wore ivory satin and carried a bouquet of fiery roses to go with my hair, and Robbie was the best man, and the church was crammed full with everyone from the village, and—'

'OK! OK!' Daniel dropped a kiss upon her mouth. 'I remember.' His voice was husky. 'How could I ever forget?' he whispered. 'You made me the happiest man alive.'

'Mummy, when is the baby going to come out?' Robbie took his head away from Cathy's prominent stomach and looked up earnestly into her face. 'I want to play with it.'

'Soon.' Cathy smiled at her son, then gazed up lovingly into Daniel's face. 'Very soon.

'Perhaps we'd better be getting back to the cottage,' she murmured. 'This ground *is* beginning to feel a little hard, and besides, I want to finish off making the curtains for the nursery.'

The three of them walked hand in hand across the lawn of Langforde Hall. So much could happen in a year, Cathy thought. She gazed lovingly across towards Daniel, who was chatting to a very happy-looking Robbie. Marriage to the most wonderful man alive, becoming a mother again…

She placed a protective hand over her stomach and thought of the baby that would be born within the next few weeks. Daniel would make the most wonderful father—he had already proved that true with Robbie—and he had certainly made the most wonderful husband.

I have no worries, Cathy thought, with something approaching amazement. None at all. Even Gary and his problems had been taken care of—Daniel had seen to that; amazing what a decent job and a little positive influence could do.

They walked through the tall wrought-iron gates. Daniel opened the car door for Robbie, then lifted the boot and stowed the picnic basket safely inside. He held out his hand towards Cathy. 'Coming?'

She glanced back at the grandeur of Langforde Hall. It looked magnificent in the late-afternoon sunshine. One day it would be their family home, but not yet—not for a long while...

'Yes,' she murmured, smiling into her husband's eyes. 'Of course.'

COMING NEXT MONTH

ONE MOTHER WANTED by Jeanne Allan

Allie and Zane had once loved each other intensely. When they meet again and Allie offers to marry Zane so that he can win custody of his daughter, hope springs eternal. Can he now make Allie his wife for real?

SUBSTITUTE FATHER by Janelle Denison

Lauren's goal is to help an orphaned boy meet his hero, Rafe Dalton. Rafe isn't ready to be a hero but Lauren hopes that when he opens his heart to the boy he'll also find room for her!

TO TAME A BRIDE by Susan Fox

(Rebel Brides)

Lincoln is the first man to ever stand up to Maddie St. John. He also discovers that beneath her prickly pride is a vulnerable woman. Could Lincoln be the man to tame her?

RICO'S SECRET CHILD by Lucy Gordon

Julie is shocked to find that her new boss is the man she left eight years ago. Rico is as tender-hearted as he once was. Is now the time to tell him the truth about why she left?

Available from 5th November 1999

Available at most branches of WH Smith, Tesco, Martins, Borders, Easons, Volume One/James Thin and most good paperback bookshops

COMING NEXT MONTH

MILLS & BOON®

Enchanted™

THE CONVENIENT FIANCÉE by Jessica Hart

Polly was glad to do her friend Simon a favour and act as his fiancée. Then they found something new in common— chemistry. There was only one obstacle to a *real* engagement—Simon's real fiancée.

BRIDEGROOM ON APPROVAL by Day Leclaire

(Fairytale Weddings)

Hanna went to the ball to bring home a husband—on a trial only basis. Marco had been looking for a business deal, until he saw Hanna! They were married by midnight but he still had to convince her this marriage could last a lifetime.

THE BOSS'S BRIDE by Emma Richmond

Claris knew that acting as stand-in-mum to her boss's baby god-son would be challenging. Yet she and Adam were developing a taste for parenting, and for each other, and beginning to wonder what would happen when the baby went home to his mum and dad.

HUSBAND POTENTIAL by Rebecca Winters

Fran didn't want a husband and Andre didn't want a wife. To keep the undeniable sense of intimacy between them under control, Andre feigned unavailability. Would Fran feel so safe when Andre revealed he had husband potential after all?

Available from 5th November 1999

Available at most branches of WH Smith, Tesco, Martins, Borders, Easons, Volume One/James Thin and most good paperback bookshops

COMING NEXT MONTH

THE SOCIETY GROOM *by Mary Lyons*
(Society Weddings)

Once, they'd had a passionate affair. When they met again at a society wedding Olivia thought she'd lost all interest in Dominic FitzCharles—until he made a surprise announcement…

SLADE BARON'S BRIDE *by Sandra Marton*
(The Barons)

When Lara Stevens met Slade Baron an overnight flight delay led to a tempting invitation. Who would Lara hurt if she accepted? He wanted her and she wanted…a baby.

GIBSON'S GIRL *by Anne McAllister*

Gibson was fascinated by the shy and beautiful Chloe. Should he seduce her? Gib was tempted. Should she resist him? Chloe had to. Eventually it became a question of who was seducing whom!

MARRIAGE ON TRIAL *by Lee Wilkinson*

Elizabeth had insisted on an annulment - and disappeared from Quinn's life. Now he'd tracked her down and claimed she was still his wife. Did he really love her, or did he want revenge?

Available from 5th November 1999

Available at most branches of WH Smith, Tesco, Martins, Borders, Easons, Volume One/James Thin and most good paperback bookshops

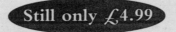

4 FREE

books and a surprise gift!

We would like to take this opportunity to thank you for reading this Mills & Boon® book by offering you the chance to take FOUR more specially selected titles from the Enchanted™ series absolutely FREE! We're also making this offer to introduce you to the benefits of the Reader Service™—

- ★ FREE home delivery
- ★ FREE gifts and competitions
- ★ FREE monthly Newsletter
- ★ Exclusive Reader Service discounts
- ★ Books available before they're in the shops

Accepting these FREE books and gift places you under no obligation to buy, you may cancel at any time, even after receiving your free shipment. Simply complete your details below and return the entire page to the address below. *You don't even need a stamp!*

YES! Please send me 4 free Enchanted books and a surprise gift. I understand that unless you hear from me, I will receive 6 superb new titles every month for just £2.40 each, postage and packing free. I am under no obligation to purchase any books and may cancel my subscription at any time. The free books and gift will be mine to keep in any case.

N9EA

Ms/Mrs/Miss/Mr ....Initials..
                                                                    BLOCK CAPITALS PLEASE
Surname ....

Address ....

....

....Postcode................................

Send this whole page to:
UK: FREEPOST CN81, Croydon, CR9 3WZ
EIRE: PO Box 4546, Kilcock, County Kildare (stamp required)